S I A

Peking Man and
Upper Cave Man

Mapa

Pithecanthropus,
Meganthropus,
Solo (Ngandong)

AUSTRALIA

FOSSIL MAN
AND OTHER
FOSSIL PRIMATES

Lilli Mautner

The Evolution of
MAN

A Brief
Introduction
to Physical
Anthropology

HOLT,

RINEHART and WINSTON, Inc.

New York

A Brief
Introduction
to Physical
Anthropology

The Evolution of

MAN

Gabriel Ward Lasker

Wayne State University

Preface

How did such a being as man come about? What is happening to change him? And what are his chances for survival and change as the prospects of overbreeding, war, and biological failure or success challenge him? For many serious readers, curiosity about the past and future is given urgency by the hope that intelligent intervention by man may affect his destiny. Although there are numerous works on other aspects of these questions, the author believes that a brief introduction to the evolution of man, past and present, can help focus interest on the biological aspects. While physical anthropology is obviously concerned with the story of man as an evolving organism, it encompasses interrelated topics ranging from diseases of fossil man to growth patterns of children; and each of these studies has its own techniques and rationale.

The purpose of this text is, in part, to relate seemingly diverse studies to a central theme: human evolution. It is hoped that this tale has been told in such a way that it will appeal to interested laymen as well as to students of anthropology. The book is meant to be an introduction to the concepts, and even to some of the technical terminology and procedures, of physical anthropology for both kinds of readers. Facts, interpretations, speculations, and opinions are woven into the story, but it is hoped that these are clearly identified for what they are. Short chapters proceed from subject to subject, as might be the progression in an introductory course; subsequent sections frequently depend on definitions introduced in earlier parts rather than repeating material for the sake of making individual chapters self-sufficient.

About one half of the book is devoted to human evolution in the past, especially the study of our origins. The other half deals with those evolutionary processes in man that produce and preserve inherent variation. After describing the place of man in the organic world, and especially among the primates, we proceed to the testimony of fossils: the character of the early men and the evidence concerning when and how they lived.

Since evolution today can best be understood within the larger framework of genetics, the science of natural inheritance, the genetics both of individuals and of populations is briefly taken up. The topic of race is introduced here, at a point when the previous discussion of genetics has prepared the reader for awareness of the ephemeral nature of the association of specific traits and the way in which frequencies of traits may alter in one population or another. Changes in racial traits that can be accounted for by movements from one environment to another—that is, transitory and reversible effects of human plasticity—are summarized.

Although the author has found this sequence of topics suitable for the subject, other sequences are possible. Some readers may wish to relate physical anthropology more closely to cultural anthropology: having considered the nature of culture, they may proceed to the question of how an animal endowed with capacity for it could have evolved. For them, social aspects of animal behavior—a fascinating subject with an ever-growing body of evidence—may be the starting point; and the focus of attention may be the mechanisms of such evolution, the process of continuing evolution, the flux of races, and, perhaps, specifically racial problems of contemporary interest. For this approach questions of human prehistory and the fossil record may be of lesser concern.

Still other emphases or orders of procedure may be suggested, perhaps by some pronounced interest manifested in the community or by the relationship of the physical anthropology course to other courses. For example, its study may be linked to that of archeology; in that case, the identification and interpretation of skeletal remains would be stressed. Or, where physical anthropology is taught as a branch of biology, linked to a concern with hygiene, the emphasis would be placed on problems of normal growth and of body composition and physique.

My purpose, then, has been to assure that the principal topics of physical anthropology are at least introduced. The coverage has been kept comprehensive, leaving to the ingenuity of the teacher enlargement on those topics that he wishes to stress. Because of the brevity of this text, teachers who use it will have ample opportunity to enlarge on its contents in their lectures and to supplement it with additional suggestions for reading and, perhaps, laboratory assignments. In addition to the references given at the end of each chapter, the specific references to sources of information in the text will suggest other supplementary readings.

The author's debts are wider than these references indicate. Although, where testimonies or opinions differ, he presents those views that to him seem most valid, and although he makes no mention of advice or criticism with which he disagrees, he is deeply sensible of the debt he owes the authors of many works not specifically cited, to his teachers (including E. A. Hooton, C. S. Coon and S. L. Washburn), and to fellow members of various Wenner-Gren Foundation summer seminars and other conferences. He is particularly grateful to those who have read and commented on all or part of one or another draft of the manuscript including, among others, anthropologists Stanley M. Garn, William W. Howells, Felix Keesing, John Landgraf, Marshall T. Newman and Frederick P. Thieme; the author's associates in anatomy, F. Gaynor Evans and Ernest Gardner; a geologist, Maurice Rosalsky; the author's father, Bruno, and his wife, Bernice. I wish to thank those who are acknowledged in the legends, and also the following persons who offered help with illustrations: J. Lawrence Angel, Melvyn J. Baer, Charles R. Carpenter, Sir Wilfrid E. Le Gros Clark, Luther Cressman, S. M. Garn, James Gavan, Martin Gusinde, William W. Howells, Lois Wells Mednick, Hallam Movius, Neil Tappen, Phillip Tobias, S. L. Washburn and his son Stanley Washburn who drew Figure 9-13 on page 89, and Sir Solly Zuckerman.

Berkeley, California   G. W. L.
November, 1960

Contents

8 · Evolutionary Processes and Paleontological Principles 63

9 · Some Fossil Primates 71

1 · Physical Anthropology as a Field of Science

Physical Anthropology Defined

"Anthropology," from the Greek *anthropos,* man, and *logos,* knowledge, means the study of man. Physical anthropology is the study of man's evolution and biological variation, and encompasses the study of manlike fossils and fossil man. A considerable variety of ancient bones of manlike types are now known, and their interpretation will be considered later. Much of the progress made in this direction is the work of archeologists and paleontologists, students of the old. Archeologists have provided the excavated bones of early man, and paleontologists those of earlier animals that may have been ancestral. Paleontology is largely responsible for our knowledge of the mode of evolution, developed in studies on other lines of animals with more complete fossil records than those of man. Paleontologists in conjunction with historical geologists have also provided the necessary dates (see Chapter 7) for a study of the tempo of human evolution.

Physical anthropology has a distinct place largely because it unites the results of such studies with those of the anatomist. Comparative anatomy and embryology yield many ideas concerning the origins of human characteristics. A special field of comparative zoology, the study of the nonhuman primates (which include the apes, monkeys, and some other animals), has defined man's biological place in nature and permits evolutionary studies

1

of the soft parts of the body not preserved in fossils. Tests performed on living monkeys and apes provide examples of physiological functioning, nervous responses, and even the thinking of earlier animals similar to man.

Physical anthropology also encompasses racial differences among men. In what do racial differences consist? How have they arisen? Do they determine the way people behave or think? While these are questions for physical anthropology, those concerning people's behavior and thought are in the wider framework of social science, and the contributions of cultural anthropology, psychology, and sociology are involved. Both in the natural and in the social sciences some of the greatest advances of recent years have been made in respect to just such questions whose answers must be sought through several disciplines. As physical anthropology turns to the older science of zoology for pertinent knowledge of non-human animals, such as monkeys, and for a wide range of studies in genetics, so zoology itself, in its more recent development, has a debt to chemistry and physics among other sciences.

Another problem for physical anthropology is the nature of hereditary differences between men and the way such differences originate. How is genetic variability established, augmented, or lost? To answer such questions physical anthropologists study the processes of human genetics, especially the genetics of so-called normal variations, such as the blood groups. Blood groups may differ from individual to individual, but they are transmitted from parents to children in definite ways. But what probably concerns the anthropologist most about human inheritance is the genetics of populations: the factors that lead to genetic stability or change in a local group of primitive men, for example.

Furthermore, physical anthropology encompasses several kinds of problems that use techniques first developed in evolutionary and racial studies. Anthropometry, the measurement of man, is properly a branch of physical anthropology. Man measurement is essential in the study of growth and is also used to assess variations between men that result from environmental influences during the growth period.

Finally, variations in human physique, whatever their cause, challenge the physical anthropologist for a description and an explanation. Sometimes the answers have practical significance, as in, for example, the relation of physique to disease. And as man literally hems himself in, his clothes and his chairs, cars, and cockpits provide a challenge for the application of physical anthropology to the design of man's physical environment.

Recent Trends in Physical Anthropology

There are four respects in which a revolutionary new spurt has taken place in physical anthropological studies since the mid-nineteen forties. The first was the discarding of many exploded ideas. The concept of pure racial types, for example, was shown to be sterile. (Unfortunately, such notions continue to remain current in, and to confuse, public opinion.) Second were the great methodological and technical advances that made it possible to probe successfully into questions that could not formerly be tackled with any assurance of objectively reliable results. Thus, for example, carbon-14 dating was introduced, physical and chemical methods for the study of deeper structures of the body were developed, and photographic and x-ray techniques were adapted to the examining of human form and composition. Third, the period saw a trend toward closer alignment of physical anthropology with genetics and other biological sciences and also with other sciences of man. Individuals trained in physical anthropology are now serving as human geneticists on medical faculties, investigating fertility and sterility in man—with all its complex sociological aspects—studying physical adjustment and maladjustment, and engaging in many other activities. The core problem of physical anthropology remains the effort to understand human variation and evolution, modified in man by the many cultural factors that direct the changes and affect their rates.

The fourth phase of the postwar advances was the application of proven anthropological techniques and their modification to meet practical requirements. World War II itself provided many opportunities for such new applications. It was necessary to clothe millions of men and women, using a limited number of uniform sizes; planes, tanks, and trucks had to be designed to accommodate live human beings; remains of war dead needed identification; geographic medicine was a concern of our far-flung armies; and the question of paternity was an aftermath of war. Physical anthropologists in uniform tackled these problems and returned at the war's end with new theoretical questions raised by these attempts to apply existing knowledge (White, 1952).

At the same time the new theoretical emphasis required the development of new techniques. Statistical methods were refined; blood grouping became a necessary skill, as did genetic analysis. One group of physical anthropologists concentrated on a new technique of body build classification, that of somatotyping. For a while it seemed that physical anthropology might break up into a series of new disciplines, but by now it seems clear that the subject field will not lose its unity. No other discipline stands ready to undertake the synthesizing of human biology. Biologists, physicians, anatomists, historians, demographers, geneticists, and psychologists continue to raise questions about man's origin and to look for a key to their common problems. Physical anthropologists hope to find that key through a unity of purpose but diversity of approach. The processes of human evolution and differentiation require for their understanding not only the development of general principles but also the application of scientific methods and the further development—or borrowing from other disciplines—of specialized skills.

The Study of Man

It is usual today to divide the study of man into a series of separate though linked disciplines. Psychology, rural sociology, international economics, ancient history, and cultural anthropology—to mention just a few of these fields—are so diverse in the techniques they apply that specialists in them sometimes lose sight of the common problems they face. Even in anthropology each scholar tends to specialize on one approach. The study of the history of a language may be quite different, not only in subject but also in character, from the study of the history of marriage customs or of pottery. Furthermore, all these differ from the history of man's anatomy. But ultimately all history depends on the kind of animal man is and the way he has come to be. The biological evolution of a being who will talk, stay mated, and cook food in the pots he has made for that purpose is basic to the history of language, marriage, and pottery.

The differences in these cultural characteristics between the Englishman and the Eskimo, the Samaritan and the Seminole, the Hottentot and the Hun, can be studied only by methods of cultural history, but the very existence of culture and the possibility of cultural difference are dependent on a special kind of organism with suitable tongue and vocal chords for talk, suitable hands to make pots, and a reproductive rhythm suited to regulated mating. Few animals have any of these traits; none except man combines all of them with adequate mental capacity to develop culture. While the development of these capacities and the evolution of an organism possessing them must have depended on the growth of culture itself, the evolution of a suitable culture bearer came first. Man's animal history is as old as his cultural history or older if we concede a biological preadaptation to culture. That animal history therefore must be considered a necessary preface to the story of man.

GENERAL REFERENCES

Korn, N., and H. R. Smith, 1959, *Human Evolution: Readings in Physical Anthropology*. New York: Holt, Rinehart and Winston, Inc. Short articles by competent scholars, collected from popular writings, chapters of text books, and, occasionally, technical reports. Useful in giving examples of various points of view on many of the topics in physical anthropology.

Montagu, M. F. Ashley, 1960, *Introduction to Physical Anthropology*, 3d ed. Springfield, Ill.: C. C. Thomas. Presents some topics in greater detail than the present work.

2 · Evolution, the Dynamic Process

Evolution, a Fact

Scientists consider as factual an observation that is capable of being observed by others. A factual statement is one that contains enough information so that anyone can see its truth for himself, or at least can test its veracity by explicit techniques and known instruments without reliance on hidden assumptions or occult knowledge. Human evolution is a fact, not just a theory. It has the same kind of status as any other "fact" studied by scholars.

The process of sexual reproduction ensures that each successive generation differs from the last. The relatives of a newborn infant sometimes say, "He is the image of his father." At most, however, the child merely resembles his parent. One never sees a child who is identical in every feature to either parent (see Fig. 2-1). Thus, from looking at photographs one can see that some persons look quite different from the way either of their parents appeared at the same age. Ordinarily, the term "evolution" is used only for continuous changes that have gone on for many generations, but the process is the same as the change from father to son. In essence, therefore, this is evolution.

It is true that such differences may be difficult to see in a strange people. To some observers, "All Chinese look alike." This is because the features in which the Chinese differ from our own group are so strikingly evident that we may fail to notice the variations

7

Fig. 2–1. Photographs of a father and his son taken in 1902 and 1942 respectively. There is notable similarity in some features such as the nose, but even aside from the differences between the Russian and American uniforms it is easy to distinguish the father from the son on the basis of width of the jaw, shape of the face, and details of the region about the eyes.

existing among them—variations that they find perfectly adequate for identifying their acquaintances. With suitable photographs of Chinese or Japanese or Siamese, we can test the statement that there are differences from generation to generation in these peoples, too. For example, the skinfold that gives the almond-eyed appearance to the Chinese has innumerable variations and individual differences (see Fig. 17-1).

Evolution Defined

If it were not for such differences, however slight they may be, there could be no evolution. By *evolution* is meant any change in hereditary endowment through time. It consists of all the processes through which some inherited qualities develop and permeate the species and others regress or fail to be preserved. Both may go on simultaneously, while still other hereditary features may persist and be transmitted unmodified from parents to children.

A child sometimes resembles one of his grandfathers or grandmothers but not his father or his mother. Whatever degree of resemblance he has inherited from earlier ancestors must have come to him through his parents, but the influence does not operate with predictable exactness. No one can predict in what member of a large family a noteworthy physical feature of a grandfather will reappear or whether it will necessarily reappear at all. Such a hereditary characteristic may occur in only some of the offspring, express itself to various degrees, or become modified. The process of evolution is similarly irregular. Indeed, when there are no changes whatever in environment or habits and the population does not intermarry with others, one may see merely small chance fluctuations in physical characteristics from generation to generation without continuing evolution in one direction. In nature there are many instances of so-called living fossils such as the opossum and the horseshoe crab which have remained little modified. Slow evolution, however, would of necessity be rare in man and especially so in recent times with our high population mobility and changes in living conditions. We have plenty of proof for the fact that evolution is at work among us.

Evolution through Increased Numbers of One Part of the Population

A further example of evolution as a fact is the continuous changes in the proportion of different groups in the United States. Some groups—the American Indians, for example—have decreased in numbers. In 1600 there were 900,000 to one million in the continental United States. The number of Indians shrank to about 350,000 by 1920 and is now close to half a million (La Farge, 1960).

On the other hand, certain of the immigrant groups from Europe have multiplied steadily as well as rapidly. Changes in the proportions of the groups that make up the world population go on generation after generation as is evident in the facts and figures about differential reproduction rates for various peoples, accessible in United States census reports, publications of various other governments, the United Nations, and other sources. These are facts that anyone who is interested can verify for himself and that, to the extent that populations differ genetically, demonstrate ongoing human evolution. One used to hear talk of a "yellow peril," the result of supposedly high reproductive rates in Japan or China. This concept rested on an error, of course—namely, the confusion of biological and cultural values. If the high reproductive rate of one race could be considered a peril to other races, then the peoples of Asia and Africa might have spoken of a "white peril." In the last 300 years the population of Europe has increased sixfold, and this number should be doubled again to take account of increases in Europeans living outside Europe (Sax, 1956). In the same period the population of Asia has increased only fivefold and that of other groups even less. This means that the average person of the physical types present in Europe 300 years ago has today several times as many descendants in the world as has a hypothetical average non-European man of that day. Europeans colonized North America, Australia, New Zealand, and to lesser extents South and Central America, Africa, Asia, and Oceania. The result was a significant evolutionary change. Such change is not a problem in itself. There is no yellow peril, white peril or black peril, but only the peril of numbers.

Relationship of Theories of Evolution to the Facts

But what about the long stretch of past evolution? What facts have we to demonstrate that it took place? What human changes have occurred in the last 50,000 years? And what humanoid evolution occupied the Pleistocene period, the glacial ages of the preceding million or so years? "No one has ever found the missing link," one hears the uninformed say. By now we have much fossil evidence for all sorts of links in human ancestry. Besides skeletons of men, apes, and monkeys we have numerous fossils of a wide variety of intermediate forms, and the quantity of such finds has increased with the years. As we shall see, some of these are from apelike men, some are from manlike apes, monkeylike apes, apelike and even manlike monkeys, and there are also monkeylike lemurs, mammal-like reptiles, reptilelike amphibians, amphibianlike fishes, and other similar evolutionary links between living forms. Our problem is not in finding missing links as such; it is in establishing the genetic interrelationships of fossil forms, the order in which they occur, and the way in which they lived. To solve this range of problems it is important that the search go on for specimens of more complete skeletons and variant types from various places and geologic times.

Even though evolution is a fact, rather than a theory, the theorist can still make important contributions to physical anthropology. Isolated facts are meaningless without theory. We may describe a thousand shells on a beach and be right about the material composition and shape of each of them; but how they came to be there requires a theoretical reconstruction of the forces that formed and deposited them. Not chance, but a traceable combination of circumstances, left them at the edge of the sea. This "theory" differs from a series of "facts" by suggesting a process that can be seen through its results, rather than observed in itself at first hand. There is adequate scope for the elaboration of such theory.

History is reconstruction of the past. The study of human evolution is in part a similar reconstruction. But evolution also goes on today, and the study of ongoing evolution has the same bearing on its past phases as political science, economics, and other social studies have on human history: Evolutionary theory assists in reconstruction and also uses what is known of processes of the past in helping to explain forces and movements passing so close to us that sometimes they defy accurate observation. Therefore, while history in some of its phases is merely narrative, the study of evolution is not merely historic in this sense but in addition comprises all the elements of a complete and rounded field of inquiry. Evolution is both history and science. Like all sciences it collects data and also develops theories—that is, explanations of how evolution works in general. The development of these theories and their application to the interpretation of our past is a proper part of our story. The development of the science of genetics, and the application of its principles to natural populations, permits us to answer the question of how human evolution could—and could not—have occurred.

Thus, we may still speak of "theories of human evolution" even when we recognize evolution itself as a fact.

Two events stand out in the early history of the development of the theory of human evolution: One is publication of Charles Darwin's *Origin of Species,* the other, of Gregor Mendel's *Investigations in Plant Hybridization.* In both cases the discoverers were biologists; in neither case was the discovery first related to man. Charles Darwin, the author of the idea of evolution through selective survival, for many years said little about man except that, as a result of his studies of animals, light would be thrown on the origin of man. Alfred Russell Wallace, a naturalist who came on the idea of natural selection independently of Darwin and who presented it jointly with Darwin in July, 1858, also said nothing of man at the time; indeed Wallace had some doubts whether natural selection applies to man in the same way that it does to animals. Nevertheless, both critics and champions of natural selection immediately saw that the theory could very well apply to man.

The other striking event in the development of the early history of evolution was the observation of a regular pattern of inheritance based on transmission of particles (genes) from the parents rather than on a mixing of parental blood or other fluid (see Chapter 13). The conclusions of the Augustinian priest, Gregor Mendel, who experimented with crossbreeding peas, were presented in 1865 but were never understood in his lifetime because of the boldness of his abstract conceptions and the fact that he used statistical methods not prominent in most branches of science until many decades later. The years following Mendel's experiments saw the development of knowledge of the cell (begun by T. Schwann in 1847) and of the mechanics of cell division and reproduction (started by the pathologist, anthropologist, and statesman Rudolf Virchow in 1855). By 1900 the climate of opinion among biologists was ripe for an adequate theory of genetics, and Hugo De Vries, C. Correns, and E. Tschermak independently formulated Mendel's laws. Working on his own and in ignorance of Mendel's work, each of these three botanists rediscovered Mendel's principles and showed that they apply to numerous plants and are general laws. Within two years a physician, Sir Archibald Garrod, published similar statistical findings in pedigrees of human families with hereditary metabolic diseases.

12 ◆ EVOLUTION, THE DYNAMIC PROCESS

By the early 1900's the theory of evolution had become a fact supported by fossil finds, implemented by knowledge of particulate inheritance and already advanced by the study of biochemical genetics in man.

GENERAL REFERENCE

Barnett, S. A., ed., 1958, *A Century of Darwin*. Cambridge, Mass.: Harvard University Press. Chapters 1, Theories of Evolution; 2, Species after Darwin; 6, Darwin and the Fossil Record; and 7, Darwin and Embryology, are especially recommended.

3 · The Organic Basis of Life

The Basic Units of Life: Chromosomes and Genes

Before exploring in more detail the facts of human evolution, it will be well to consider both the nature of life and man's place in nature. A knowledge of the rest of the animal kingdom will permit us better to interpret man's own history and status. All life shares some properties, and we may best begin with some species very unlike our own. We shall start with the origin of the life process and the simplest forms of life and progress toward man's "poor relations," the monkeys and apes.

Few scientifically trained people today deny that man could have evolved from nonhuman animals. Indeed, there is plenty of fossil evidence that such a process did take place. Likewise, it can be shown that all but the simplest organic forms could have evolved from simpler ones. The other facts we need in order to explain evolution are evidence, first, that in a suitable environment some unit of life is capable of producing an exact image of itself with all the original functions and, second, that occasionally such images will be slightly inexact in one way or another but will, in turn, be capable of reproducing themselves.

The nuclei of cells contain granules that tend to absorb certain dye pigments; thus stained they can be identified under the microscope. When cells are undergoing division (*mitosis*), the deeply stained granules are seen to be arranged in small elongated bodies, usually definite in number for any given species. These rodlike

15

bodies are called *chromosomes*. In various organisms it has been shown that particular sections of chromosomes are specifically concerned with the transmission and development of particular hereditary traits. These sections, or elements, are called *genes*. The gene is such a unit as we postulated as essential to evolution. It can produce an image of itself, and the image is occasionally inexact.

Ordinary genes are submicroscopic in size. They are so small that the whole human complement, enough to determine half of all an individual's hereditary makeup, is crowded into each spermatozoon, the male sex cell. As we shall see in Chapter 13, the gene is a segment, variable in length, of a chromosome with a particular arrangement of its molecular parts. A chromosome is thus analogous to a fragile fiber whose segments, the genes, act like—and in fact are—complex molecules of organic compounds.

Chemical Evolution of Complex Organic Compounds

How could the materials present in the world before life existed synthesize such complex organic compounds? So far as we know, the naturally occurring complex organic compounds of today are the results of life processes: Life seems always dependent on prior life. Imagine, however, a time when there was no life—a time, that is, when there was no process by which, after death, complex organic compounds were regularly and inexorably reduced to simpler forms. The rot, decay, and fermentation that reduce organic compounds to simpler compounds and chemical elements can occur only as the result of the life processes of microorganisms. The simpler substances of alcohol and vinegar derive from plant starches and sugars by organic fermentation. Similarly, yeasts, molds, or bacteria are required to decompose flesh or plant to water and simple gases. Without fermentation the grape would keep forever. A time of nonfermenting grapes never existed, however, because yeasts, molds, and bacteria evolved before the vine.

Since there was nothing, before life, to cause complex carbon-containing compounds to decay, compounds would have become more complex, not simpler. We assume that one of these complex compounds achieved the status of an organism, able to reproduce

16 ◆ THE ORGANIC BASIS OF LIFE

images of itself. What we call life began with this substance, as it utilized and broke down the surrounding substances for the creation of its descendants.

According to the view propounded by Harold Urey (1952), professor of chemistry at the University of California, the original atmosphere of the earth was composed of methane, ammonia, hydrogen, and water instead of, as it is now, nitrogen, oxygen, carbon dioxide, a little hydrogen, and traces of other substances. Methane is a simple carbon compound, ammonia is a simple nitrogen compound, and hydrogen is an element. In the presence of electric energy, such as would be provided by lightning, an atmosphere composed of these three gases produces a variety of compounds, including formic acid; the situation is then propitious for the formation of *amino acids,* the chemical building blocks that are found in all forms of life. Whether this is actually what happened cannot now be determined, but lightning or ultraviolet energy from the sun could conceivably have effected the first steps of chemical synthesis.

All theories of the natural origin of life postulate that some form of intense energy—light, heat, radioactivity, ultraviolet irradiation, or electricity—converted simple one-carbon compounds to chemical compounds with multiple carbon atoms. Laboratory experiments have demonstrated several methods of bringing about this process. Amino acids and other complex substances result from the action of sunlight on formic acid or formaldehyde with ammonia, nitric acid, or nitrates. Acetylene in the presence of suitable metallic catalysts can form large organic molecules. Cosmic or other radiation can form compounds of two, four, or more carbon atoms from simpler ones.

In each of these theories, the continued application of energy would lead to ever more complex carbon compounds. Some of these compounds would have the special property, well known in chemistry, of speeding the transformation of other substances into its own kind (autocatalysm). In this way random physical-chemical changes would become systematic: Changes would occur in particular directions at definite rates. Other physical-chemical processes, such as crystallization, determine special arrangements of molecules and would have initiated an orderly changing system of organic compounds.

Some writers refer to this process as chemical evolution to contrast it with the evolution of living things (Calvin, 1956). Such a distinction is arbitrary, however, dependent in turn on an arbitrary definition of "life." We can understand the "origin of life" but cannot point to its occurrence at some particular time. We can understand the kinds of physical-chemical processes that convert the simplest carbon compounds into amino acids and proteins, without knowing which of these were important. Indeed, in some billions of years of time, chemical evolution toward living results may have been modified by relatively minor events.

The Origin of Life

Proteins are still more complex than amino acids. They consist of combinations of these acids and are present in all plants and animals. Every living thing must either synthesize proteins or live on organisims which do; even the simplest plants are capable of several stages of synthesis. Until life began, the nonliving environment could have held quite complex substances, for there would have been no life to break down such compounds by decay. Once, however, any complex of carbon-containing molecules achieved the ability to reproduce itself, it would be alive, but its descendants would begin to use up all the natural *substrate,* the chemical food, on which they grew. If some descendant were modified (mutated) in the direction of being able to grow on some simpler substance, this form would have an advantage and would multiply in a world in which the original "food for life" had become scarce (Horowitz, 1945).

Each time this happened the descendants added a new capacity to synthesize and, at the same time, the world lost some complex organic substance achieved by nonlife processes. The gap between the most complex nonorganic substances and the simplest forms of life increased until it is now so great that some find it difficult to accept the possibility of conversion of the former into the latter. The gap could hardly have been jumped by a single event; a plausible view postulates that many steps were involved. In time the last step, originally a purely chemical synthesis, began to take place within the organism and became a biological process. The increasingly long chains of life processes progressively eliminated the complex chemically synthesized substrates on which rudimentary forms of life depended. Thus, with the disappearance of both the rudimentary forms of life and the complex freely occurring compounds, the gap between the kinds of chemical substances found within living things and independently of living things constantly increased. We shall see that natural selection and *particulate inheritance,* the independent inheritance of single specific traits, can explain the development of complex forms of life from simple ones. They also permit a plausible theory of the origin of life itself. The theory holds that the gap between living and nonliving was once much smaller and that all living things today are the result of a long period of evolution of life forms and devolution of chemical substrates. A natural selection between systems of organization led to survival of the most efficient, life.

The Meaning of Differences in Animals

Although man differs in some respects from all other beings of the world, he nevertheless shares many of his characteristics with one or another animal. In general, the various kinds of animals can be grouped according to the degree to which they resemble us. Such a list was compiled by the Swedish naturalist Linnaeus in 1758. This work is the basis of modern taxonomy, or scientific classification, even though it was compiled before biologists recognized that degrees of similarity often stem from degrees of relatedness and that the differences between kinds of animals are explained by divergent evolution. Any system of classification based on analogies of form is likely to range some chance similarities as equivalent with similarities that derive from genetic relatedness. It is therefore surprising that, in the conversion of the Linnaean system from a simple classification of forms to one meaningful in evolutionary terms, zoologists have hardly modified the basic nature of Linnaeus' grouping of animal forms. Evolution has left such clear traces in the animal kingdom that Linnaeus, although intent only on classification by similarity in form, unwittingly followed these traces. His system is to that extent *phylogenetic*—that is, it reflects the origins of forms. Species with recent common origins are grouped together.

The Capacity to Reproduce

All types of living things possess one property not shared by objects devoid of life. They have the capacity to reproduce. That is, given the right environment, they can create essentially identical images of themselves. As the essential quality of living matter is reproduction, the essential quality of the offspring must be this same capacity to reproduce. Our knowledge of how reproduction takes place has been greatly enhanced by a series of experiments on minute organisms such as the bread mold, *Neurospora*. In these experiments it is seen that the units of heredity, the genes, appear to act like those organic chemicals, the enzymes, that serve to speed up certain chemical transformations. It was fairly obvious in theory, even before it could be demonstrated, that the genes are composed of complex organic molecules of the same kind as those of enzymes. Unlike enzymes, however, genes, or as we shall see, series of them, can unfold and serve as templates or molds for the production of more of their own kind from the surrounding substrate. In some respects they act as enzymes without losing the quality of life, being active as catalysts in speeding important biochemical syntheses in the tissues without themselves being altered in the process. Free enzymes in the blood are like genes, but molecules of free enzymes are folded in on themselves and are unable to act as templates for forming images of themselves.

The Role of DNA

On the basis of experiments on the chemistry of the minutest parts of cells—the new science of cytochemistry—Watson and Crick (1953) have reconstructed a picture of the genic material of life. On the basis of their examination of the microscopic diffraction, or bending, of x-rays by the molecules of the cell nucleus, they see the essential material as being in a substance called deoxyribonucleic acid, which they call DNA for short (see Fig. 3-1). Their

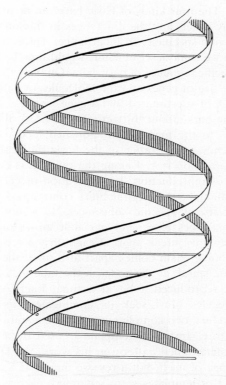

Fig. 3-1. DNA. A double spiral of sugar molecules connected by base bars of pairs of molecules. (After Watson and Crick, 1953.)

picture of the chromosome consists of a double spiral made up of sugar molecules on the outside and other substances on the inside. If one twisted a longitudinally striped ribbon, one would get such a pattern: The border stripes would represent the sugar; the inner part would represent cross-links composed of four substances. Molecules of these four substances must always occur in pairs. From what we know of the size and shape of these molecules, and the way the chemical bonds would fit the parts together to form the spiral, only four types of pairs would be possible.

One such pair of these molecules, with its attached sugar molecules, occurs at each level along the spiral and is called a basic nucleotide bar. The four kinds of basic bars can be arranged along the spiral in any order, and the differences in this order—the base sequence—provide specificity in inheritance. The gene of pedigree genetics, which we shall describe later, would thus be a segment of DNA with a specific sequence of basic bars. On the basis of estimates of the probable size of genes and the molecules of substances composing the DNA, it is estimated that a gene would consist of a fair number of basic bars, about thirteen. The twisted ribbon is somewhat analogous to the magnetic or punched tape of the modern computing machines. The order of the basic molecules represents the genetic information stored along the tape. This code is "read" in the process of reproduction. In duplication of cells by division and self-reproduction, each spiral must come apart at the bonds between the pairs of specific substances. It is not now known exactly how this takes place, but one half must "unscrew" from the other or they must break apart at each turn. Very possibly only a part of the double chain comes apart at a time; the process progresses down the spiral, as the code on the tape is "read," and the complement is reproduced a bit at a time. Each of the pair of basic bar molecules must seek its complement anew from the substrate to produce two complete and identical spirals where only one existed before. Just as a template is used by a machinist to impose the predetermined pattern on his work, the DNA does not produce an image of itself, but a reverse image. If a coupled complementary pair of templates were separated, each would produce an image of its complement; hence the whole material would be reproduced, and the result would be two identical chromosomes.

GENERAL REFERENCES

Oparin, A. I., 1957, *The Origin of Life on the Earth,* 3d ed., translated from the Russian by Ann Synge. New York: Academic Press Inc. Discusses the evolution of organic substances, systems, and organisms.

Tax, Sol, ed., 1960, *The Evolution of Life, Its Origin, History, and Future.* Volume I of *Evolution after Darwin.* Chicago: University of Chicago Press. The contribution by Hans Gaffron, pp. 39–84, discusses the origin of life.

4 · Early Evolutionary Pathways toward Man as Reflected in Surviving Forms

The Smallest Living Things

A *virus* is almost the simplest living thing we can imagine. It is about the size of a chromosome, seems chemically related to the gene, and possesses the same primary capacities. The minute viruses are so small that they will pass through a filter and can be seen and measured only in an electron microscope, where their shape is outlined as an enlarged shadow in a stream of electrons. Yet they have the ability to reproduce—only, of course, in the right environment (in our bodies or those of other organisms). When they reproduce in numbers they cause reactions in human tissues, making us ill with a specific disease, such as poliomyelitis or mumps. When they spread to another host they reproduce more or less true to kind and produce polio or mumps respectively in the person who is being infected. The bacteriophages, a particular kind of virus, actually live parasitically within a bacterium where they multiply until they destroy their host. All viruses are parasitic, in fact, and, like some parasitic plants and animals, may have developed from higher forms by loss of functions that are performed for them by their hosts. Although not truly primitive, bacteriophage suggests by analogy what primitive life may have been. Viruses contain reproducing genetic material and, within a host, can produce more virus.

23

The Animal Kingdom

Among the living things, those which require organic food and oxygen for respiration are called *animals*. Their movements are in response to outside stimuli, hence they are described as "sensate"; that is, animals have feelings and, although it is difficult for us to know how they feel, we can see that they respond rapidly to stimuli. Man is thus obviously an animal: He moves and feels. The animals range from tiny one-celled organisms to quite complex beings. A feature of the animal kingdom—which all animals use in some generations and some (including man) use in all generations—is bisexual reproduction. That is, reproduction is not simply the production of an image of one parent but the recombination of elements inherited from two parents.

In bisexual reproduction the chromosomes are paired. Each member of the pair may have different genes. In all the cells of animals there is a complete complement of chromosomes, with both of each pair present—with one exception. The exception is that in the sex cells at the time of reproduction, only one of each pair is present; that is, only half of the chromosomes of each parent are involved. Furthermore, each of a pair of chromosomes may be different, and it is a chance matter which of a pair of chromosomes is involved in the recombination in the offspring. In bisexual reproduction, therefore, offspring will differ from each other and from each parent. The mechanism of bisexual reproduction thus provides for great variability.

Throughout evolution, as each major adaptation has been obtained the animals which possessed it have increased in number and in kind. This diversification is called *radiation*. Furthermore, the radiations have been compounded with each new adaptation. The result might be envisioned as a hierarchy consisting of groups in which the oldest and most fundamental modifications characterize inclusive groups while later and minor modifications characterize species and other subgroups.

Each level in the taxonomic hierarchy of the animal kingdom has a special name, beginning with races (or subspecies) and going up to grades. Thus animals whose bodies are made up of more than one cell, and in which different cells fulfill different functions, form

CLASSIFICATION OF MAN

Species
Homo sapiens
Including all postglacial and perhaps some earlier races of man.

Genus
Homo
Including Neanderthal man, Rhodesian man, and Solo man.

Family
Hominidae
Including *Pithecanthropus erectus* from Java and the similar Peking man.

Superfamily
Hominoidea
Including the great apes, gibbons, and australopithecines.

Suborder
Anthropoidea (or *Simii*)
Including the Old and New World monkeys.

Order
Primates
Including the Prosimii, such as tarsiers, lemurs, and tree shrews.

Infraclass
Eutheria
Including rodents, Carnivores, etc.

Class
Mammalia
Including marsupials and egg-laying mammals.

Subphylum
Vertebrata
Including fishes, amphibians, reptiles, and birds.

Phylum
Chordata
Including a few aberrant forms.

Grade
Metazoa
Including all other multicelled animals.

a major division of the animal kingdom, a separate grade from the one-celled animals.

The Chordates

The major division of grades are called *phyla* (singular, *phylum*). Among multicelled animals man belongs to the phylum of the chordates. These bilaterally symmetrical animals are distinguished by having, at some time during their life, a flexible cord, the notochord (from the Greek word *noton,* the back) down their backs. They also have a spinal cord, but it is the notochord rather than the spinal cord that distinguishes the Phylum Chordata.

Of the chordates, the most numerous group shares still other features with man. This subphylum is the *vertebrates* and includes the fishes, amphibians, reptiles, birds, and mammals. These forms have a spinal cord with a brain attached at one end. Together these structures form the central nervous system, which coordinates movement and sensation. In addition, vertebrates have a well-developed vertebral column (the spine) to surround and protect the spinal cord. They also have an internal skeleton of bone or cartilage to surround and protect such organs as the brain and sense organs, and to extend the limbs. The vertebrates, including man, regularly have two pairs of limbs or, as in snakes and whales, some evidence of descent from animals which did.

Mammals

One distinct category of vertebrates have breasts and nourish their young with milk. Subdivisions of phyla are called *classes* by biologists; one is the class Mammalia (having mammae, breasts). Because of the way *mammals* nourish the young after birth, they establish social relations between female and offspring. Social relations, thus characteristic of the whole class, are especially useful to the mammal *man* for the generation-to-generation transmission of culture through learning. The birds (class Aves) have two features in common with the mammals: Their young, after hatching, remain dependent on their parents, and they are warm-blooded animals. The internal control of the body's environment gives birds and mammals the capacity for undiminished activity the year around. The body temperature of some mammals fluctuates somewhat, but even the bear during hibernation does not undergo a slowing of vital processes to the extent characteristic of fishes or reptiles similarly exposed to the cold. In cold environments mammals therefore manage better than reptiles; no crocodiles and few varieties of lizards and snakes are found outside the tropics.

One distinction between mammals and birds is that mammals have hair (lacking or reduced in the adult of some giant forms, such as the whale and elephant, which need it less for warmth) whereas birds have feathers. Another important difference is that mammals nurse their young and birds do not. The birds, on the other hand, have evolved such a diversity of methods for nourishing the young that it is somewhat surprising that, in the course of evolution, none of the mammals has lost the peculiar adaptation which gives the class its name, and taken up one of the modes of rearing used by birds. One possible explanation is that, besides being an ideal food, milk also contains substances called antibodies that help protect the nursling from disease.

Egg-laying Mammals and Marsupials; Placental Mammals. Within the class Mammalia are three so-called infraclasses. The first is that of the *monotremes.* These mammals, in common with reptiles and birds, lay eggs as their mode of reproduction. The duck-billed platypus and the spiny anteater, both of Australia and the latter also of New Guinea, are the only two extant mammals belonging to this infraclass. The existence of the infraclass suggests that the mammals acquired the capacity to nurse before any of them substituted live birth for egg laying.

The *marsupials* constitute a second infraclass of mammals. This group is somewhat more widespread than egg-laying mammals and, besides numerous types in Australia, including the kangaroo and the teddy-bear koala, also includes the American opossum. Marsupials are *viviparous;* that is, they give birth to live young. The newborn are very dependent, however, and must find their way to a pouch on the mother's abdomen, where they can attach themselves to her nipples and remain within the pouch until they are adequately developed to reemerge.

Man belongs to the third infraclass, Eutheria, placental mammals which develop by a special process in which the egg is shed from the mother's ovary, is fertilized, and then implants itself into the walls of the mother's womb. The *embryo*—the early stage of development of the organism—produces on the wall of the womb a *placenta,* a temporary disc of tissue permitting interchange of fluids between mother and offspring. While the bird's or reptile's egg must contain yolk enough to nourish the embryo until hatched, as well as a device for storing innocuously the waste products of the developing embryo, the placental mammal utilizes the physiological mechanisms of the adult mother for these functions and for supplying oxygen to the tissues of the embryo. In this way the offspring can be protected until more fully developed than the offspring of egg-laying animals. Other animals, including some snakes and fishes, are viviparous and have the capacity to harbor the eggs within the mother's body until ready to hatch, but only in the eutherian mammals is there a placenta capable of permitting a long intrauterine development and the birth of large infants.

GENERAL REFERENCE

Romer, A. S., 1941, *Man among the Vertebrates,* 3d ed., Chicago: University of Chicago Press. Comparative anatomy in evolutionary perspective. Chapters 1, 3, 5, and 9 describe the origins of fish, amphibians, reptiles, and mammals, respectively.

5 · The Order Primates

Defining the Primates

The study of the mammals is especially pertinent to human evo-lution because one order of eutherian mammals, the primates, com-prises those groups, living or extinct, with which man shares such outstanding traits as the tendency to enlargement of the brain.

It is difficult to define the primates. W. W. Howells (1944), pro-fessor of anthropology at Harvard University, says that the whole order "is unspectacular, simple and generalized, which is, paradoxi-cally, its main characteristic." Primates have a pendulous penis (males) or breasts on the chest (females), collarbones, rings of bone about the eye, and freely movable thumbs or first toes. Each of these characteristics, however, is shared with some other animals.

The primates are an ancient group; of the living mammals, only the marsupials and two placental orders (the insectivores and the carnivores) have left fossils of greater antiquity. Furthermore, al-though we may think of our kind as highly developed, the primates are primitive; in many respects primates retain generalized mam-malian features and have evolved less than other orders. This very primitiveness is one of the reasons why the primates have few features distinguishing them from other mammals. Instead, primates are perhaps best distinguished by certain tendencies that are more marked in some than in other members of the order. These include keen vision (although, in man, glass lenses are rapidly becoming a regular part of the visual apparatus), grasping hands and, some-times, feet; and, most important of all, high development of the brain

29

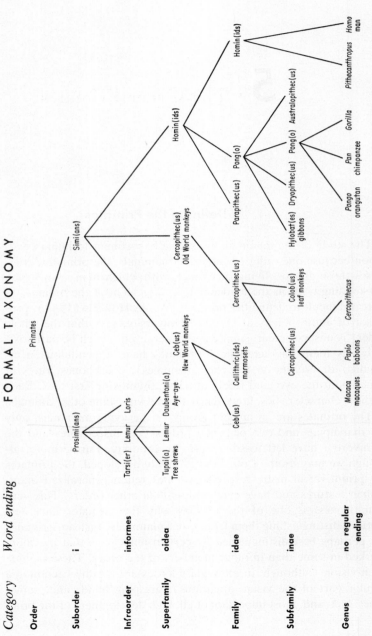

FORMAL TAXONOMY

Category	Word ending	
Order	*i*	Primates
Suborder		Prosimi(ans) / Simi(ans)
Infraorder	informes	Tarsi(er) Lemur Loris
Superfamily	oidea	Tupai(a) Lemur Daubentoni(a) / Ceb(us) / Cercopithec(us) / Homin(ids)
		Tree shrews Aye-aye / New World monkeys / Old World monkeys
Family	idae	Ceb(us) Callithric(ids) / Cercopithec(us) / Cercopithec(us) Colob(us) / Parapithec(us) Pong(o) Homin(ids)
		marmosets / leaf monkeys
Subfamily	inae	Cercopithec(us) / Hylobat(es) Dryopithec(us) Pong(o) Australopithec(us)
		gibbons
Genus	no regular ending	*Macaca* *Papio* *Cercopithecus* / *Pongo* *Pan* *Gorilla* / *Pithecanthropus* *Homo*
		macaques baboons / orangutan chimpanzee / *Pithecanthropus* man

To classify the primates, drop the ending in parentheses and add the appropriate ending from the second column.

Fig. 5-1. Some representatives of the non-human primates of today. A: Tree shrew. B: An African lemur (*Galago*). C: Tarsier. D: Macaque. E: Gibbon. F: Chimpanzee. (from W. E. Le Gros Clark, *History of the Primates*, 1953. Courtesy of the Trustees of the British Museum).

and its functions. It may help to delimit the primates and set the stage for a study of man's place in nature if we list the other surviving members of the order (see Fig. 5-1 for some representatives). Various authorities group these in different ways, but the system devised by the paleontologist Simpson (1945) is as widely used as any, and we may accept it as satisfactory for our present purpose, with only very minor modification.

A Classification of the Primates

Any system of classification must be based on degrees of similarity. The question is, similarity in respect to what? The answer of taxonomists, the zoologists who specialize in this field, is similarity in respect to traits that best show common origins. Biologists cannot always identify such traits, but those who study the fossils will take extinct as well as living forms into account in their scheme and thus have a richer material for classification. We can start with Simpson's names for various animals even though further evidence is constantly being discovered that may alter ideas about their lines of common descent.

The Prosimii or "Pre-Monkeys"

The first in Simpson's classification is the suborder Prosimii, literally "pre-monkeys" (comprising the so-called Lemuriformes, Tarsiiformes, and Lorisiformes). The lemurs (Fig. 5-2) of Madagascar are, perhaps, the most characteristic of the surviving Prosimii. The late Professor Earnest A. Hooton (1946, p. 15) of Harvard University, who had a habit of disowning his verses, claims to have received the following description of the lemurs from an anonymous correspondent.

> The lemur is a lowly brute;
> His primate status some dispute.
> He has a damp and longish snout
> With lower front teeth leaning out.
> He parts his hair with his comb-jaw,
> And scratches with a single claw
> That still adorns a hinder digit

Fig. 5-2. Ring-tailed lemurs of Madagascar. (From W. E. Le Gros Clark, *History of the Primates,* 1953. Courtesy of the Trustees of the British Museum.)

> Wherever itching makes him fidget.
> He is arboreal and omnivorous;
> From more about him, Lord deliver us![1]

Some of the other Prosimii are also specialized for particular modes of life. The members of one large, nearly tailless, family, the Indriidae, subsist on leaves and other vegetable matter for the digestion of which they possess an inordinately long and labyrinthine bowel. Another prosimian from Madagascar, the Aye-aye, has peculiar ratlike front teeth permitting it to gnaw open limbs of trees in search of grubs which it impales on its spindly middle finger. The little mouse lemur sleeps the summer through while nourishing itself from a special fat pad at the base of the tail, much as camels can subsist on their humps. The Lorisiformes (Fig. 5-3) of Asia and Africa are given to night prowling for insect prey, and the tarsier of the Philippines and Borneo apparently lives entirely in this way. Although the tarsier (Fig. 5-4) is equipped with elongated feet, to give it spring when jumping, and enormous eyes relative to its small body, a number of details of the anatomy are similar to those of "higher" primates: The organs of smell are reduced, while those of sight are emphasized. As in man and the owls, the eyes look to

[1] Earnest A. Hooton, *Up From the Ape* (New York: Macmillan, 1946). By permission.

Fig. 5-3. *Loris.* These slow-moving creatures have large eyes for night vision. (Courtesy of the Zoological Society of London.)

the front rather than to either side as in the horse. Carriage horses are equipped with blinders to emphasize forward vision, but they have not evolved the two-eyed view of tarsier and many other primates.

The tree shrews (Fig. 5-5) are included by Simpson among the Lemuriformes, but formerly they were not even considered to be primates. They resemble the insectivores, the mammalian order which includes the tiny voracious American shrews, especially in anatomy of the skeleton. The very primitiveness of both the primates and Insectivora—the slowness of their evolution in most respects—should lead one to expect that small generalized forms of each might resemble one another quite closely.

The Monkeys of Central and South America

The rest of the primates, the suborder Anthropoidea, consist of the monkeys, apes, and man. Although members of this suborder have much in common with one another, the monkeys of Central and South America—the New World monkeys—are clearly distinct from the rest, in that they have an extra premolar tooth on each side of each jaw, and the nostrils of some species are relatively wide apart. These Cebidae, as the New World monkeys are called, also vary among themselves in structure and habits. The little

Fig. 5-4. Tarsiers. Arboreal animals, they have good night vision and live on insects. (Courtesy of the Zoological Society of London.)

marmosets retain the prosimians' tendency to have litters, usually giving birth to twins, whereas the rest of the Anthropoidea usually have their young one at a time. Marmosets are omnivorous: Their diet includes some live insects, grubs, and spiders. Another New World form, the night monkey, has enlarged eyes for nocturnal vision. Other New World monkeys, such as the cebus (the "organ grinder's monkey") (Fig. 5-6), the large gangling spider monkey, and the huge-throated, loud-mouthed howler monkey, have vegetarian diets: Some live chiefly on leaves, others eat more fruits. Some New World primates (including the cebus, the spider and the howler monkeys) can grasp with the tail. The prehensile tail actually

Fig. 5-5. Tree shrew, a small, primitive, insect-eating primate. (From W. E. Le Gros Clark, The Foundations of Human Evolution, 1959. Used by permission of the Oregon State Board of Education.)

has skin-ridge patterns on the tip like man's "fingerprints." Patterns in the skin of the fingers and toes, palms and soles, are found throughout the Anthropoidea.

Old World Monkeys

The Old World Anthropoidea are grouped in different ways by different authorities, the scheme selected usually depending on

Fig. 5-6. A New World monkey, the cebus, one of those which grasps with its tail. (From W. E. Le Gros Clark, *History of the Primates*, 1953. Courtesy of the Trustees of the British Museum.)

whether the writer believes man to be more closely related to the great apes than to the gibbons or the Old World monkeys.

The Old World monkeys are usually considered as a super-family or a family which is divided into two subfamilies; one of these, the Colobinae, consists of the various leaf-eating monkeys of Africa and Asia. These colorful varieties are seldom seen in the zoos of the United States because in general they do not adapt well to captivity. They have large stomachs which enable them to digest bulky low-calorie leaf foods. On the average, the jaws that relate to this diet are less jutting than in monkeys with a more varied diet, but in bones and, presumably, muscles of the limbs, tail, and back, the leaf monkeys do not differ much from the other Old World monkeys, the Cercopithecinae.

The subfamily Cercopithecinae contains the macaques, the monkeys most widely used in laboratory tests because, like all the higher primates, their constitution and physiology are so similar to our own. They are susceptible to most human diseases and exhibit much the same symptoms as man; the development and production of the Salk polio vaccine depended on this fact.

Wilson

Fig. 5-7. Baboon, a predominantly ground-living Old World monkey. (From W. E. Le Gros Clark, *History of the Primates*, 1953. Courtesy of the Trustees of the British Museum.)

The macaques, baboons (Fig. 5-7) and other Cercopithecinae show several superficial dissimilarities. Baboons grow as big as wolves, some vervets are as small as squirrels; the baboon has a long snout and short tail, the vervet a short snout and long tail; and different species of macaques vary in size, snout, and tail. Nevertheless, these genera of Cercopithecinae are known to be closely related to each other because, when housed together in zoos, they mate with one another and have healthy offspring (Zuckerman, 1933).

Within this subfamily we find a wide range of diets and ways of life. Cercopithecinae are arboreal and live primarily on vegetarian diets of fruits and leaves, but the largest of these monkeys, the baboons, forage on the ground; troops of from 9 to 185 have been counted. Baboons eat roots, shoots, and rarely insects or even small animals. The limbs of baboons are adapted for quadrupedal (four-footed) gait, and therefore resemble those of other ground-living quadrupeds.

The Cercopithecinae are widely distributed in Africa, Asia, and Malaysia. The one form now found in Europe, the Barbary macaques of Gibraltar, would probably be extinct were it not for the occasional reintroduction of animals from North Africa. They are semitamed by the British garrison, some of whom believe superstitiously that the British will retain the "rock" only as long as the "apes" remain.

Although they are similar in general appearance, there is no connection between Old World and New World monkeys. Wild-living African green monkeys are found on the island of St. Kitts in the West Indies, but these are known to have been brought to St. Kitts by man within the last 300 years or so. Two English anatomists, Ashton and Zuckerman (1951), took advantage of this fact to find out whether there had been any evolutionary changes in them during this period, and found that the St. Kitts monkeys are, on the average, slightly different from the African descendants of their common ancestors.

The Gibbon

Those who consider man more similar to the anthropoid apes than to the monkeys usually class him with the former in a separate superfamily, the Hominoidea. There are four types of extant apes which share the term "Hominoidea" with man. (Formerly the baboons were sometimes called "dog-faced apes" because of their

Fig. 5-8. Gibbon. Arms that are much longer than the trunk or the legs, and prehensile hands (and feet), make him well adapted to brachiating habits. (New York Zoological Society Photo.)

size and prominent snout, but they belong among the monkeys, with whom they share many features, such as the types and details of the teeth. Furthermore, as we have noted, baboons are able to interbreed with other Cercopithecinae.)

The smallest of the four anthropoid apes (family Pongidae), the gibbons (Fig. 5–8), are relegated to a subfamily of their own, the Hylobatinae. The native habitat is in Southeast Asia. They are the most agile trapeze artists of all the primates, although they share this skill with the great apes, the spider monkeys, and, to some extent, schoolboys. A caged gibbon has been seen to swing from one arm and pluck a luckless bird out of the air in midflight. They are

A CLASSIFICATION OF THE PRIMATES ♦ 39

generally vegetarian, however, although occasionally they may indulge a fancy for insects, a bird's egg, or even a bird.

The gibbon is also able to walk on his hind legs. On the ground he is ungainly because he must use his long arms like crutches or hold them over his head to keep them out of the way. On a limb, however, the gibbon can run like a tightrope walker, using his arms in lieu of a pole or parasol. His bipedal gait is obviously quite different from man's: He is unable to extend his legs and must keep them bent. Only man can goose-step.

The Orangutan

The other Asiatic ape is the red-haired orangutan of Sumatra and Borneo. He also is a tree-top dweller who is adept at swinging by his arms. His legs are punier than those of the other present-day great apes. The orangutan's diet is vegetarian and includes the delicious wild fruits in which the region is rich, such as the durian (which has a foul smell like that of overripe cheese).

The Gorilla

There are two African great apes, the gorilla and the chimpanzee. Anatomically they are more similar to each other than either is to the orangutan.

The gorilla, by far the largest primate, is relatively scarce. Some live in the lowlands of West-central Africa, the remainder in the mountains at the headwaters of the Congo (Fig. 5-9). The differences between the two kinds of gorilla are not great, and were it not for some hundreds of intervening miles they would probably interbreed. There are few sizable trees in the mountains of Eastern Congo; the gorillas there live on the ground, proceeding chiefly on all fours, with the foot sole-down. (Fig. 5-10). The lowland gorilla has similar feet, perhaps a little less manlike. The long forelimb makes the gorilla posture semierect. In quadrupedal walking the hand is used with knuckles down. Despite the forested habitat of the lowland gorilla, the adult male is too big to swing by his arms in the trees with the females and young. He is strong enough, however, to hold his own on the ground with any animal that might attack him. His mode of life is somewhat reminiscent of the bears, and both can easily rear on their hind limbs. A hundred years ago Du Chaillu (1861) wrote that gorillas will rear on their legs and loudly

Wilson

Fig. 5-9. Gorilla, largest of the primates. (From W. E. Le Gros Clark, *History of the Primates*, 1953. Courtesy of the Trustees of the British Museum.)

thump their chests. Some of his reports seemed so fantastic that his contemporaries were convinced Du Chaillu had never seen a live gorilla and they scoffed at the possibility, since adequately confirmed, that gorillas will charge at a man, stop short, rear up, and beat their chests. As far as we know, the diet of the wild gorilla is purely vegetarian, that of the mountain gorilla being chiefly bamboo shoots, wild lobelia, and succulent plants that grow at those altitudes. Perhaps partly because of their great size—some weigh 600 pounds —and consequent ground living, the gorillas are in many ways the most manlike of the great apes. This need not mean, however, that man is phylogenetically more closely allied to the gorilla than to any of the other living anthropoid apes.

The Chimpanzee

The chimpanzee (see Fig. 5-1) is the best known of the great apes. It has a more extensive range in tropical Africa than the gorilla, and some zoologists have recognized several species on the basis of differences in color. Some smaller, or pygmy, chimpanzees are found south of the Congo River. Much like the gorilla, but more agile, the chimpanzee scurries about the trees, swinging by his arms, or walking on the outside of his feet, while progressing on all fours (or on three of them). Nissen (1931) lists 34 varieties of plants—leaves, fruits, and flowers—that one group of chimpanzees eats at one season of the year. The chimpanzee's lips are free, and it can produce a range of facial expressions by moving the fine muscles of the face. It can also make a variety of vocal sounds, but cannot really be taught to talk, although several attempts have been made to teach chimpanzees to do so.

The Relationship of the Living Great Apes to Man

The great apes resemble man in the details of most bones, the brain, teeth, and other parts, and even the blood groups. Nevertheless, one should not underestimate those important respects in which the great apes are more specialized than man, or those in which man more closely resembles the gibbon, Old World monkeys, or more primitive primates. The great apes have callouslike skin on their bottoms (called ischial callosities), which may be an adaptation to sleeping seated, and special sexual skin in the female, which changes according to the stage of the reproductive cycle. Man and some monkeys lack these two special areas of skin. Professor William L. Straus, Jr., (1949) of Johns Hopkins University has listed numerous traits of the musculature and skeleton that associate man less with the great apes than with other Old World simians.

It is illogical to believe that man has descended from any living type of pongid or cercopithecid. All other primates have much shorter generations than man (chimpanzee females start to bear young at about the age of eight), which means that they have gone through even more generations and hence have had more opportuni-

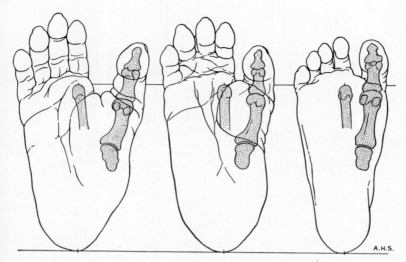

Fig. 5-10. Feet and part of the foot skeleton of (*left to right*) chimpanzee, gorilla, and man. The human foot, that of an Australian aborigine accustomed to walking barefoot, has a longer heel and less mobile great toe than that of great apes, but is in general similar to that of the mountain gorilla. (From A. H. Schultz, "The Physical Distinctions of Man," *Proceedings of the American Philosophical Society,* 94(5), 1950. Courtesy of the author and the Society.)

ties for evolutionary change, in the interim since we shared common ancestors many millenia ago. While man was busy becoming an efficient biped, the anthropoids, apparently simultaneously, perfected the mechanism for brachiation—arm swinging.

GENERAL REFERENCES

Hooton, E. A., 1942, *Man's Poor Relations.* New York: Doubleday, Doran. An easily read and well-illustrated description of the living nonhuman primates.

Straus, W. L., Jr., 1949, "The Riddle of Man's Ancestry," *Quarterly Review of Biology,* 24:200–223. Reprinted in *Yearbook of Physical Anthropology, 1949.* New York: The Wenner-Gren Foundation, 1950, pages 134–157. Evidence from living primates is used in evaluating different interpretations of man's origins.

Osman Hill, W. C., 1953, *Man's Ancestry: A Primer of Human Phylogeny.* Springfield, Ill.: C. C. Thomas. A simple account of the evidence from comparative studies.

6 · Primate Behavior: Non-human and Human

Although we cannot hope to find human progenitors among them, the study of the living nonhuman primates is nevertheless an important part of physical anthropology. Our interpretation of the evolutionary history of the skeleton—for which we do have the evidence of fossils—depends on our understanding of its role in the whole living body; to study this we must compare the variety of anatomical arrangements in the primates and other animals of today. More important, the aspect of life in which we are most interested—behavior—can be studied only in living animals, and the evolutionary sources of human behavior can best be approximated in animals most like us.

Behavior of the Howler Monkey

Unfortunately, few satisfactory studies of the behavior of non-human primates in the wild have been published. Several of the best are reports by Professor Charles R. Carpenter, a psychologist at Pennsylvania State University. One (Carpenter, 1934) reports a visit to the Barro Colorado Biological Experimental Station in Panama. Fifty odd years ago Barro Colorado Island was formed from a point of land when the water level was raised behind the Gatun Locks during construction of the Panama Canal. All the animals present at the time the canal was built have been isolated in this microcosm, and their descendants are a closed fauna within the precincts of the island. Carpenter found little groups or colonies of red howler monkeys on the island, and he could locate each group in the morning when they howled. He then watched them all day. An average group consisted of 17 animals: 3 adult males, 7 adult females, 3 infants, and 4 juveniles. The age distribution is no doubt chiefly the result of the equilibrium between birth and death rates, but the unequal sex ratio is, at least in part, maintained by the "ostracism" of some adult males. Such males are forced to live alone and are driven away when they approach and attempt to join a group. The proportion of various ages is relatively constant, however, as is the preponderance of females among the adults. The unequal sex ratio seems to correspond with the capacity for sexual arousal of the adult male, thus providing sexual satisfaction and social balance within the group. The howler monkeys assume postures, use gestures (such as rapid movements of the tongue), and make noises that serve to stimulate other members of the group to specific activities: sexual behavior, movement to a new group of trees, or aggressive deployment to repel another group or a single male. Each group maintains a definite territory within which it moves about as a unit. Other students have revisited Barro Colorado Island since Carpenter's studies and have observed that, although the total howler population has fluctuated, and the number of colonies increased, the general pattern of social behavior has remained unchanged (Collias and Southwick, 1952).

Social Life of Other Monkeys

Carpenter (1935) has also observed the activities of another species of New World monkey, the spider monkey (Fig. 6-1), in the relatively inaccessible tropical forest on the border between Panama and Costa Rica. The social behavior of these animals is somewhat different from that of the howlers. They live in groups of up to 40 individuals, the main group being made up of smaller temporary subgroups—some of males, some of females, and some of both. As with the howler monkey, there are many more females than males in the groups but there is less difference in the behavior of the two sexes; females as well as males may advance toward a human in-

Fig. 6-1. Spider monkey. The prehensile tail and the feet are used as extra hands. (New York Zoological Society Photo.)

truder and attempt to drive him off by making noises and dropping dead sticks from the trees over his head.

No published study of any Old World cercopithecid monkey is as adequate as that of these New World ceboids. Professor (now Sir) Solly Zuckerman (1932) has watched baboons in captivity, and Carpenter (1942) has studied macaques transported to a small island off the coast of Puerto Rico. The baboon male manifests dominance behavior; there is grouping of females about a male and occasional fighting among the males; the macaque behavior is similar, the supremely dominant male preferring only one female consort at a time, and various males may successively possess a female in heat. These Old World monkeys differ from the howler, however, in that the social groups are often larger and, when baboons or macaques are enclosed in a limited space, they behave much more aggressively: Males treat the females as their own and sometimes fight with other adult males that come too close to the females. It is possible to overemphasize the competetive behavior, however, and new studies based on still unpublished observations and motion pictures by Professors S. L. Washburn and B. I. DeVore of the University of California will cast more light on the significance of such social behavior as protection of the group from predators, mutual grooming, assistance to infants, and browsing as a herd.

The Gibbon "Family"

Professor Carpenter (1940) has also studied the social life of free-living gibbons in Siam. These hominoids resemble man in their grouping behavior. The average "family" consists of one adult male and one adult female with an infant and about three juveniles; we do not know how permanent gibbon monogamy may be. At times both males and females live alone temporarily. The gibbon family, like the band of the howler monkeys, occupies a circumscribed region, and the members stimulate responses in each other by the sounds they make and by their movements. Male and female gibbons are of nearly equal size, and the males are not markedly dominant over the females.

Great Apes in the Wild

The great apes are much harder to study in their natural habitat. Orangutans apparently live alone or in very small groups. Chimpanzees travel in larger groups, of about four to 14 animals, and seem to have social relationships differentiated on the basis of sex, age, and probably individual characteristics (Nissen, 1931). Gorillas are rare and inadequately studied in the wild; they may travel in groups with one or several adult males. Carl Akeley (1923), who conducted an African expedition for the American Museum of Natural History in New York, on one occasion saw a number of female and young mountain gorillas together with three or four old gray-backed males. Gorillas and baboons are the largest representatives of the Cercopithecoidea and Hominoidea respectively, and both have socially dominant adult males which are physically much larger than the females. These similarities appear to be parallel developments explicable as one kind of adaptation to ground living or rather to ground as well as tree living.

Culture, a Human Phenomenon

One of the chief contributions of anthropology to human thought is the development of the concept of culture. This word denotes the amassing of experience by man from generation to generation mainly through the use of symbolic speech. All men, even the most primitive, live in a way that is primarily learned from their forebears. No other animals do this to anything like the same extent, and Zuckerman (1932) considers culture to be an essentially human phenomenon. White's (1959) concept limits culture to the human species and attributes to man alone the ability to "symbol"—that is, to ascribe and utilize meanings. Some would define man as an animal possessing a culture, but this definition of man is not satisfactory to the paleontologist, who is concerned not with man's mental development in itself but with the evolving changes in body structure represented in ancient fossil bones. He would define the human genus, *Homo*, like any other genus, purely on biological grounds. Most anthropologists, however, would keep the zoological definition of man's family (the Hominidae), if not his genus, comprehensive enough to include all the extinct culture-making primates, whether ancestral to modern man or merely close to our line of descent.

The Biological Preconditions for Culture

Spuhler (1959) has noted that capacity for keen vision, bipedal locomotion, fine manipulation, varied diet, consciously planned sexual activity, vocal communication, and mental association are the biological preconditions for the development of human culture. In his consideration of the "Human Animal," Professor Weston LaBarre (1954) of Duke University has shown that the living non-human primates, though lacking anything like human culture, possess in varying (although always still limited) degrees most of the preconditions for culture.

LaBarre borrows a notion from Freud to explain the further evolution of humanity from such an animal. If the young males were to mature early and compete with the old for sexual access to the females (their mothers), they would be killed or driven out. Those animals whose young were slow to mature sexually, therefore, would be favored for cultural development because of the long period of dependence with its opporunity for learning. This is precisely the kind of being man is. All groups of man everywhere have an incest tabu that excludes the mother from potential mates among her sons (and hence minimizes direct sexual competition with the father). Some would consider the transmission of this parent-child tabu essential for humanity, for without it the offspring could not remain indefinitely in the parent's social group, learning ways of doing things from generation to generation. With permanent families, however, more intelligent members would be favored, successful groups would flourish, and evolving man would become increasingly "human." The chief argument against such a theory is that among nonhuman primates young and old males live in the same social groups and do not fight over access to sexually receptive females. This aspect of social behavior must have been a precondition for the evolution of man.

Playfulness as a Precondition

Playfulness, another capacity important in the development of human culture, may also be foreshadowed in some primates (Kroeber, 1948). It is doubtful that art, philosophy, and science could have developed solely as planned activities with predetermined ends. Random activities engaged in for their own sake are certainly pleasurable to the young of many other mammals as well as to humans. In man, and to a lesser extent in the chimpanzee, the delay of sexual maturity and the long period of childhood dependence provide extended opportunities for play. Man's capacity for "make-believe" is, in fact, a likely stimulus to invention. We might, in this connection, speculate about the wheel. Although it was applied to chariots in ancient times in Asia, before Columbus came to America the only wheels in the hemisphere were on little pull toys. Would American Indians have thought of the cart themselves had it not been for Europeans? Gunpowder was a toy before it was a weapon; was the bow a toy first, too?

However developed or invented, tools of any kind are frequently considered a hallmark of man. In an interesting discussion of the question Washburn (1959) shows that, on the contrary, what we think of as human evolved long after the first use of tools. That is, much of the structure of *Homo sapiens* resulted from the developing culture or protoculture of his forebears. A relatively intelligent type of primate using vocal communication for an increasing array of meanings would make many uses of social relations, and it is likely that human social life evolved together with man's biological and cultural development.

GENERAL REFERENCE

Carpenter, C. R., 1934, "A Field Study of the Behavior and Social Relations of Howling Monkeys," *Comparative Psychology Monographs*, 10(2): 1–168. A classic study of the behavior of wild-living primates.

7. Timing Evolutionary Events

Absolute and Relative Dating

The direct evidence of the course of human evolution consists of the petrified remains of man's ancestors—fossilized bones and teeth, which, in many cases, are found together with primitive human tools. In order to study these fossils and their meaning for evolution, it is important, whenever possible, to determine how long ago the bones were parts of living beings. This age occasionally can be stated in terms of years, in which case it is called the absolute date. When such dating is not possible, one frequently can determine which of two fossil forms lived first—that is, their relative dates.

The methods of dating human remains are identical with those used by geologists for dating rocks. Geologists long ago noticed that, in a succession of undisturbed sediments deposited by bodies of water, relative dates are indicated by the sequences, older beds occurring below and younger ones above. Geological chronology begins with this Law of Superposition. When fossils are found in a succession of layers, or *strata,* their relative ages are established by superposition. By the comparison of strata, place by place, region by region, and continent by continent, a complete world-wide chronology according to relative age has been constructed.

The Cenozoic Era

Geologists have noted that the rocks of the Mesozoic Era, the age of the dinosaurs, were much folded prior to the deposition of the

53

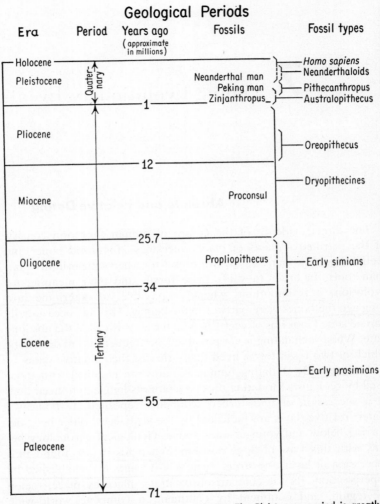

Geological Periods

Era	Period	Years ago (approximate in millions)	Fossils	Fossil types
Holocene	Quaternary			*Homo sapiens*
Pleistocene			Neanderthal man	Neanderthaloids
			Peking man	Pithecanthropus
		1	Zinjanthropus	Australopithecus
Pliocene	Tertiary			Oreopithecus
		12		Dryopithecines
Miocene			Proconsul	
		25.7		
Oligocene			Propliopithecus	Early simians
		34		
Eocene				Early prosimians
		55		
Paleocene				
		71		

Fig. 7-1. The Cenozoic Era and human evolution. The Pleistocene period is greatly exaggerated in size so that the dating of some of the fossils and fossil types can be indicated.

more recent Cenozoic sediments. From this evidence they infer the occurrence of a great revolution marked by the upthrusting of mountains, radical changes of climate, and extinction of many earlier forms of life. All the mountain ranges of the world have acquired the forms we know in the years since then. From a deposit of uranium minerals associated with strata of the beginning of the Cenozoic Era, it has been possible to ascribe to it an antiquity of approximately 71 million years. This date is estimated by means of the clock provided by spontaneous atomic disintegration of radio-active uranium. As uranium gives off its electrons, a radioactive isotope of lead is left behind, which is distinguishable from ordinary lead. The amount of uranium converted to lead per year is assumed always to have been in the same proportion to the amount of uranium present. It is therefore possible to calculate from a specimen of lead-uranium ore the approximate number of years it has existed.

Geologists divide the Cenozoic Era into two periods, the Tertiary and the Quaternary (Fig. 7-1). The former is divided into five great epochs: Paleocene, Eocene, Oligocene, Miocene, and Pliocene. These take us from some 71,000,000 years ago to the beginning of the time of the great glaciations, the Quaternary Era and its only epoch, the Pleistocene. The Quaternary is thought to have occupied roughly the last million years. The relative dates for the epochs and subepochs of the Tertiary and Quaternary are well known. The relative antiquity of rocks formed during the various subepochs has been determined from places where layers of rock can be seen to overlie one another with the older formations beneath the more recent layers. Strata can be studied in the walls of canyons or in core samples recovered by deliberate drilling.

In strata from the last several million years the amount of lead isotope obtained from uranium ore samples is so small, relative to the error of measurement, that this method cannot be used to date the deposits. Depth of strata is an unreliable measure for computing geological time, because sedimentation rates are too variable. However, for any steady event, such as weathering of soil, uplift of mountains, or cutting of river banks, we can multiply the extent of the process by an estimate of the rate at which it occurred, and thus calculate the approximate duration of the process.

The Great Glaciations of the Pleistocene

A series of related events permits the relative dating of deposits of the Pleistocene epoch, the period that has yielded all the definitely human fossils now known. This was a time of great glaciers, and these left many features. The glaciers carried large amounts of debris of various sizes from dust, sand, and gravel to boulders. Some of this material was deposited by water formed from melted ice; some was deposited directly by the ice in huge heaps called *moraines*. Various parts of a particular moraine are more or less contemporaneous. The glaciers are thought to have retreated when the rate of melting exceeded the rate at which new ice was pushed forward from the source. The retreat of glaciers was interrupted, however, by periods of equilibrium or temporary advance, and these, in turn, were followed by the formation of new recessional moraines. The intermittent formation of glaciers and their subsequent melting back into the sea resulted in the ancient beaches, formed in the Interglacial stages, that are sometimes found clearly cut in hillsides well above present high tides.

In colder periods the rivers ran slowly and deposited silt. Later, as glaciers melted during the warm interglacial periods, the rapid rivers eroded their banks. Silt was alternatively deposited and cut by new erosion, and terraces, the remains of old flood plains, were left behind (see Fig. 7-2). The Thames River in England, for example, shows remains of a series of terraces of river gravel. These include a terrace 25 feet above the present river level, formed at a time during the last interglacial period when the river was that much higher; another earlier terrace 100 feet above the present level was formed during the next to the last (Penultimate) or Great Interglacial period. Of a series of terraces in a single valley, the higher the terrace, the older; any old terrace at a lower level would be completely buried. Just as parts of one terrace are considered contemporary with other parts at the same level, so the Thames terraces are presumed to be contemporaneous with terraces approximately the same height above the present level of the Seine River in France. Furthermore, terraces the same height above the present level of the Rhine and the Somme Rivers can be considered contemporary. Correlation is reliable only in a comparatively small area, however, and cannot be established for relations among distant places: River terraces in Burma and Java, for example, were formed in the same way but not necessarily at the same times as the European.

From the glaciated areas of Europe and the river valleys of the

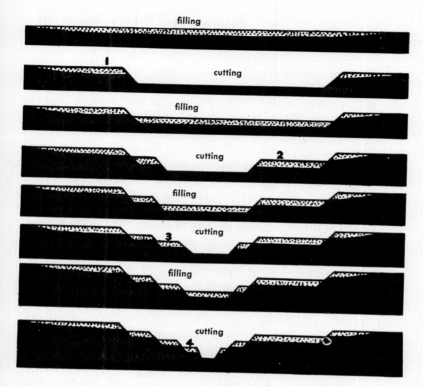

Fig. 7-2. The formation of a series of four river terraces (*top to bottom*). Near glaciers, river terraces were formed by successive filling during glacial advances and cutting during periods of melting ice and rapid rivers. The gravels of higher terraces contain remains of men of earlier periods. (From W. J. Sollas, *Ancient Hunters*, Macmillan, 1924. Courtesy of Macmillan and Company of London, Ltd.)

regions just beyond the limits of the ice it has been possible to identify four major periods of glaciation in the Pleistocene. Each of these apparently had two peaks of activity—except the last, which had three. A similar series of four major glaciations with similar subphases has been identified in North America, and it is generally believed that the two sets of events resulted from the same general climatic cycles that occurred in northern latitudes of both hemispheres.

Astronomical Theory for Dating the Pleistocene

No general agreement exists among scholars as to why the glaciers occurred, and certainly no simple theory seems adequate to explain why glaciers were present in the Pleistocene but absent during the preceding epoch. We do know that the slight periodic fluctuations in the course of the earth around the sun have affected the amount of solar radiation received in key latitudes of the northern hemisphere at different times. These may have caused changes of several degrees in average summer temperature at irregular but accurately datable times in the past. Although not explaining glaciation as such, these changes in temperature could well account for the periodic waxing and waning of the Pleistocene glaciers (Zeuner, 1958). The fluctuations in the course of the earth are dependent on several different celestial phenomena; hence, the same is true of the periods of reduced summer temperature. The last nine of these periods when, according to this theory, glacial formation would have been favored are thought to correspond well with the periods of glaciation: an Early (Günz) Glaciation with two maxima (590,000 and 550,000 years ago); an Interglacial; an Antepenultimate (Mindel) Glaciation, also with two maxima (476,000 and 435,000 years ago); a Great Interglacial period; a Penultimate (Riss) Glaciation with two maxima (230,000 and 187,000 years ago); and finally a Last Interglacial, followed by a Last (Würm) Glaciation of three maxima (115,000, 72,000, and 22,000 years ago) and by the present Postglacial period. The terms Günz, Mindel, Riss, and Würm are applied to the four periods of glacial formation in the Alps, but the more general terms can, at least tentatively, be used for glaciations and concomitant phenomena in other parts of Europe and even of North America.

Periods of low summer temperature also occurred prior to the Early Glaciation of 590,000 years ago. Along the Danube, there is evidence of Pleistocene glaciations before the Günz phase, but proponents of the astronomical theory are not able definitely to match these glaciations with particular astronomical cycles. They prefer to say that the Pleistocene began with a general cooling and the first appearance of many modern genera of mammals about 1,000,000 years ago. Among the objections to the theory is that, although a definite ultimate, Mankato, glacial oscillation is known to have taken place (about 11,000 years ago, according to the carbon-14 method, described in a following section), there is no corresponding fluctuation in the astronomical radiation curve. In any case, the estimate of the duration of the Pleistocene as about one million years is almost identical with that based on estimated rates of weathering, soil formation, and similar geological processes. The astronomical theory provides a rational, albeit tentative, basis for dating the Pleistocene.

Dating from Animal Remains and Human Artifacts

To determine relative dates in areas great distances apart it is sometimes necessary to reverse the usual method. Instead of dating fossils from the strata in which they lie, one dates strata from the fossils which lie in them. Although some forms of animals and plants have evolved so slowly that they are of little use for this purpose, others—called *guide,* or *index, fossils*—have become extinct or evolved rapidly relative to the long time periods of geology. The duration of some species was short enough for the presence of their remains in two deposits—even in widely separated parts of the world—to indicate rough contemporaneity. Furthermore, because most species of animals thrive only in certain climates, fossil assemblages aid in the unraveling of climatic sequences.

The Villafranchian animal forms—a group of fossils often found together—are of some significance in respect to the evolution of man because of the relationship of strata bearing them to strata containing fossil man. The Villafranchian period was a long one— perhaps a half-million years—of fluctuating climates, which preceded the time of extensive continent-wide glaciers. Since it was generally cooler than the preceding Pliocene and was characterized by glacier formation in the mountains, it is considered to be the early part of the Pleistocene (Howell, 1959) although the evolution of most of the cold-adapted animals occurred subsequently.

Human artifacts—things man has made and left—provide a dating criterion for the more recent periods since man's arrival. The more similar in detail two human products, the more likely that they were made by the same person or by those who learned from the same person, or at least that they belong to the same tradition and are not too far separated in time. Archeologists who excavate the remains of ancient man rely heavily on typological studies of his tools to establish chronologies.

Dating by Radioactive Carbon

Tree, plant, and animal remains offer another method of dating: the carbon isotope (written carbon-14 or C^{14}) method. It has the advantage of being independent of other techniques and of giving an approximate date in "years before present" that can be directly translated into a "B.C." or "A.D." date. The basis for this method is the discovery that the carbon of the organic compounds of all living matter everywhere seems to have a fixed ratio of ordinary carbon (C^{12}) to the radioactive isotope (C^{14}). The atmosphere contains nitrogen isotope (N^{14}) atoms that are bombarded by cosmic rays to produce the isotope C^{14}, each N^{14} atom yielding one C^{14} atom and a proton. This C^{14} combines with oxygen (O) to form radioactive carbon dioxide ($C^{14}O_2$), which, when it reaches the earth's surface, is absorbed by plants in their life processes. In turn animals get C^{14} from the plants or from other animals they eat. All living things, regardless of their age or location on the earth, have a fixed ratio of C^{14} to C^{12}. When they die, however, C^{14} is no longer absorbed, and the radioactive C^{14} slowly and spontaneously changes back to N^{14}. It has been found that one half of the originally present C^{14} atoms disintegrate in 5720 years, a fact that allows computation of the age of the sample. For example, the innermost rings of a giant redwood tree, which have not "lived" since the time of Christ, have a ratio of C^{14} to C^{12} that gives them a date of approximately 1,961 years.

This method is used for estimation of dates as long ago as 50,000 years but the proportion of radioactive carbon is very small even in contemporary material and, since it is reduced by half in every 5720 years, the earlier dates are less accurate. Furthermore, carbon, unless charred, is often lost in the process of fossilization. The best opportunities for use of the method therefore usually occur when charcoal or burnt bone is available for analysis.

Dating the Great Glaciations from the Fossils of the Floor of the Sea

In an attempt to date the glaciations of the Pleistocene epoch by a method independent of an astronomical theory, cores have been drilled from the floor of the deep sea (Emiliani, 1956). These cores contain calcareous remains of small sea animals called foraminifera. Because foraminifera are very sensitive to changes in temperature, the frequency of certain types permits an estimation of the temperature of the sea when they lived. The varying frequencies of these fossil types in different parts of the cores indicate the alternating warm and cool phases of the Pleistocene. Emiliani was also able to use a method based on changing proportions of radioactive isotopes of oxygen to plot ancient changes in temperature that have been "fossilized" in the deep sea cores.

The material of the cores contains carbon from the shells of the fossil foraminifera, and in the upper (newer) parts of the cores some of the carbon is radioactive C^{14}. From this, the last cold phase of the Pleistocene can be dated as ending approximately 17,000 years ago. This is about the same date as is obtained from the carbon of wooden stumps found in the Carey Moraine of the last glacial advance. The later cold phase represented by the Mankato Moraine in the United States, which was formed about 11,000 years ago, is not represented in the cores of the Caribbean Sea, perhaps because it was too brief in duration to leave evidence there.

Since undersea conditions alter little with time, and there is a steady settling of material on the ocean floor, the deep sea cores provide a good means of dating time periods. We know from C^{14} determinations how much sedimentation has occurred in the last 45,000 years; hence, on the assumption that earlier sedimentation was at a similar rate, we can multiply the rate by the depth of the core and so estimate the dates of previous cool and warm periods. By this test Emiliani dates the first cooling of the Pleistocene as only about 300,000 years ago. There are, however, possibilities of error in this method. Howell (1959) believes that the cold periods identified in the cores represent merely the subdivisions of the last three glaciations. For the present it may be best to reserve judgment except to say that the method confirms an antiquity of at least 300,000 years for the start of the Pleistocene.

The Fluorine Dating Method

In general, any process that goes on at a more or less fixed rate can be used for dating. One such is the rate of fossilization. Conditions of fossilization are likely to be very local, however, and the method ordinarily is useful only for determining the rough contemporaneity or sequence of bones from a single place. One way of measuring fossilization is to observe the amount of fluorine in fossil bone (Oakley, 1949). It was the discovery of the low amount of fluorine in the Piltdown specimens that eventually led to the exposure of this notorious "fossil man" as a deliberate fraud. Unfortunately, because of the varying conditions of ground water, the rate of uptake of fluorine by bones is irregular. Nevertheless, some allegedly ancient human bones have been shown to have too little fluorine to justify the great antiquity claimed for them. Other human remains whose antiquity had been questioned—among them, bones from Natchez, Mississippi, and Midland, Texas—have a chemical fossilization and fluorine content consistent with that of fossil remains of now extinct animals.

GENERAL REFERENCE

Zeuner, Frederick E., 1958, *Dating the Past,* 4th ed. London: Metheun and Company. This account of the methods and findings of geological dating, insofar as they relate to human prehistory, is considered controversial by many geologists. Nevertheless it remains the most comprehensive account of the subject.

8 · Evolutionary Processes and Paleontological Principles

Parallelism and Convergence

In interpreting the fossil evidence, anthropology utilizes principles developed on other evolutionary lines with more complete fossil records. Essentially, there are two possible interpretations favored in general by paleontologists and anthropologists for explaining the connection between two related fossil forms, or between a fossil form and an extant one. When, on the basis of the dating criteria already described, we can say which of a pair of related fossils is the earlier, it may be inferred that (1) the later form is directly descended (that is, evolved) from the earlier or (2) both are descended from some still earlier common ancestor. With more than two forms, various combinations of these two interpretations are possible. Some paleontologists array the known fossil types in a chronological sequence; others resort to the concepts of *parallelism* and *convergence*—similar evolutionary developments in disparate forms—to explain similarities by more ancient common origins. The two types of hypothesis may be diagramed simply. If A, B, C, and D represent a temporal sequence of related fossils, their family tree may take the form either of a straight palm or of a branched willow (see p. 64).

A particular characteristic may, it is true, have more than one origin. Thus, the visible effects of some of the known genetic mutants in mice, for example, are exactly mimicked by mutant genes on a different chromosome or at different places (loci) on

63

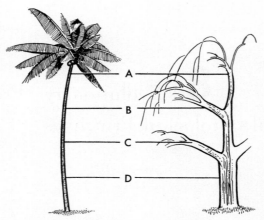

the same chromosome. Nevertheless, such similarity in effect results from parallel changes (mutations) occurring in highly similar lines. *Parallelism* in evolution also implies a similarity in biological make-up of the ancestral types. It merely indicates that the separation from common origins occurred at a previous time.

Convergence, on the other hand, implies that, under the pressure of a common force such as a change in climate, two biologically diverse organisms have come to resemble each other more closely. Convergence is ordinarily limited to a single or a few characteristics. Similarities in the eyes of some quite diverse night-wakeful (nocturnal) animals are an example. Of the two main types of retinal cells (rods and cones) only rods, which are more sensitive to dim light, are present in some deep sea fish, bats, the armadillo, some lizards and snakes, and probably guinea pigs, whales, some lemurs, and the night monkey; owls, rats, and cats have a high ratio of rods to cones. All these animals differ markedly from each other, however, in respect to other characteristics less directly related to their night life. It is improbable that any instance of evolutionary convergence has been so dramatic and complete as to hide all traces of the diversity of origins.

Adaptive Radiation

The assessment of the relationships of fossils depends on our appraisal of whether, in the length of time predicated, a change of the magnitude and kind represented by the differences would have been likely to occur, or whether the fossils more probably belong to different parallel lines of descent. We know that during rapid changes in the external environment, which open up numerous previously unexplored opportunities for animal livelihood, relatively rapid diversification (radiation) of animal forms may take place.

Adaptive radiation is well exemplified by the history of the mammals. With the geologic revolution that marked the end of the Mesozoic period and the start of the Tertiary, the great mountain systems of the world were thrown up and previous constant climates gave way to more changeable conditions. In these circumstances the cold-blooded dinosaurs and other reptiles were apparently at a disadvantage and the warm-blooded mammals with internal control of their body temperature evolved in numerous distinct lines. The rodents specialized for gnawing, the carnivores for hunting, the hoofed animals for grazing; the primates and sloths took to the trees; the whales, seals, and sea cows adapted for life in the ocean; and the bats took to the air. Furthermore, each of these mammalian orders in turn colonized several different environments and modes of life with evolutionary sublines. Many of today's mammals are far different from the primitive mammals of the beginning of the present era, the Paleocene epoch. In addition, various of the orders and suborders of mammals have undergone further radiation, branching into types adapted to different habitats. Thus, in respect to diet all the chief groups of primates include species with different dietary habits. Largely insect-eating, leaf-eating, and more or less omnivorous genera occur in each of four primary branches of the primates, and members of the fifth main division, the tarsioids, consist of a single genus which lives on insects.

Generalized and Specialized Forms

Some evolutionists have discussed the degree to which forms are capable of further diversification through evolution by natural selection. Those forms that preserve the capacity to evolve are called "generalized," while those that can survive only by a single restricted way of life (and can evolve in only one direction) are called "specialized." By this criterion man is in many ways a generalized mammal. He preserves five digits on each hand and foot and is notably lacking in such specializations as horns, tusks, wings, and hoofs. Man is specialized, however, in respect to his unusual hind limbs, being capable of rapid movement on two legs in a manner not duplicated in other two-legged animals. Man is also specialized in the size of his brain and the complexity of his neurological functions: No other animal has developed symbolic speech, for example. It is generally agreed that the retention by man of generalized features of the upper limb permitted him to manipulate things in his hands, and become a tool user.

I find the concepts of "specialized" and "generalized" less useful for understanding human evolution than do most anthropologists. After the fact, we can look back and guess at the course human evolution has taken, but looking ahead I find it hard to predict what features of today deserve the term "generalized." Perhaps it is only after a structure has given rise through evolution to a variety of new organs that we can call it generalized. Thus, the five-fingered hand is described as generalized, but the simple mammalian external ear is not, for no animals have yet evolved external ears for locomotion, touch, or the grasping of food.

The Question of Irreversibility of Evolution

A principle first enunciated by the Belgian paleontologist Louis Dollo, in 1893, and sometimes called Dollo's law, is the concept of *irreversibility of evolution*. In no instance do we know of an evolutionary process that has, step by step, led back to a type of creature exactly like some ancient prototype. We have seen, however, the re-evolution of types highly similar in one or several respects to forms that preceded. For example, the extinct flying reptiles, the pterosaurs, developed wings but eventually died out; the ability to fly was re-evolved independently in the birds and bats. It is self-evident from the laws of chance that the likelihood is most remote of a change of the natural environment in exactly a stepwise reverse order; hence an occasion for reversed natural selection would similarly be rare. Moreover, since other organisms play such a large part in the adaptation of any form of life to its natural environment, a true reversal would require the simultaneous reversal of evolution in many other organisms. Evolution is irreversible to the extent that true *atavisms,* or throwbacks to earlier forms, do not occur in detail. Viewed in the small, however, it seems to me that the next generation is almost as likely to reverse a trend as to carry it forward. Repeated and reversed mutations that manifest such single steps forward and backward are known in experimental genetics. That such reversals will not recapitulate a whole sequence is justification for Dollo's principle, but the fact does not save the usefulness of the concept of "generalized" forms as a measure of future capacity to evolve. We have no evidence for any force within the organism directing the line of its unfolding evolution (the now discredited idea of *orthogenesis*).

Evolutionary trends may be maintained, however, by the process known as *orthoselection.* The climate of the world changes gradually over long periods of time; the advances and retreats of ice ages, for example, occupied thousands of years. Such trends apply continuing selective pressures on organisms—pressures that in turn may give a direction to evolution; in other words, an orthoselection. Orthoselection in some organisms would tend to impose similar orthoselection on others.

Pedomorphism

The evolutionary status of man has been characterized not only as plastic and generalized but also as having a third more or less independent property—that of *pedomorphism,* a term meaning childlike in form. The adult man or woman displays a number of physical traits that in other animals are seen only in the young or even in the fetus—such features as the rounded form of the forehead and the delay or absence of ossification of the connections between certain bones such as the suture between the nasal bones. The great apes, on the other hand, show more developed features in these respects and are therefore referred to as *gerontomorphic* (the form of old age). Racial differences exist in respect to these features: Europeans, for example, often show gerontomorphic features, whereas some Mongoloids and the South African Bushmen have more bulbous foreheads, flat faces, and other "infantile" characteristics (see Chapter 17).

Man's pedomorphism, as we have already noted, is associated with a prolonged social infantilism that may have aided the development of language and culture.

The Varying Tempo of Evolution

The evolution of a species may be rapid at one time, very slow at another. At one time it may affect one anatomical system—say the limbs—and at another it may affect a different one, perhaps the jaws. With a change in the food supply or some other alteration in the environment, running or biting ability, for example, becomes more or less important for natural selection. This feature of evolution has been likened to a mosaic, in which independently colored bits of tile make up the total picture.

This variability in the tempo of evolution of different anatomical structures in the same line (that is, in ancestors and descendants) makes it unwise to draw sweeping conclusions concerning the relationship of two fossil forms on the basis of isolated characteristics. Instead, it is necessary to follow the evolution of whole functional systems (Washburn, 1951). Since the systems themselves evolve at different rates (Fig. 8-1), one must also take into account the total morphological pattern not only of the part but also of the whole animal insofar as it is preserved (Clark, 1955). Often the wisest response to a fragmentary fossil is suspended judgment while one searches for additional material. A few measurements considered out of context can lead the unwary anthropologist far astray.

The evolutionary trends of different systems—pieces of the mosaic—seem to have a dynamic of their own, however, and these can sometimes be studied separately. For example, from studies of comparative anatomy and function it is possible to identify some particularly striking hallmarks of man such as the bipedal gait and the relatively large and functionally effective brain. The evolutionary trends toward these characteristics, as they unfold in the fossil record, are referred to as *bipedalization* and *encephalization*. The mosaic pattern of evolution led to bipedalization after the evolution

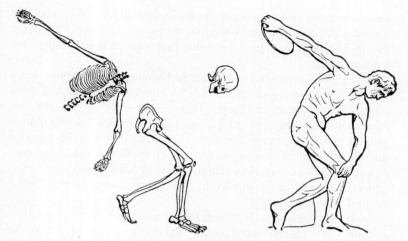

Fig. 8-1. Separate parts of the human skeleton and the functional systems with which they are associated—the trunk and upper limbs, the locomotor system, and the head with its brain and sense organs, for example—have evolved at different times and at different rates. (From Felix M. Keesing (after Washburn, 1951), *Cultural Anthropology,* Holt, Rinehart and Winston, 1958. Courtesy of the author.)

of a manipulative apparatus with hand and eye coordination, but human encephalization was late and rapid.

Extinction

Direct relationships are often too easily assumed. Some animal forms survive—especially in out-of-the-way places—long after their ancestors have given rise to quite different descendants elsewhere. Indeed it would be sheer chance if any fossil man now known were in fact your very ancestor. With average fertility a person would leave two billion offspring in 31 generations, and an average person would be descended about two billion different times by different lines of descent from an average dweller of the fourth century A.D., twice as many generations ago. Yet the statistics are deceptive because in some cases many lines would reconverge from each ancestor and in other cases no lines. No one can claim descent by any line from Saint Agnes, for instance, because she had no children when she was martyred in about 304 A.D. Furthermore, if there were any direct descendants of *Australopithecus africanus,* they are certainly not from the individual we know by the fossil skull from Taung; the skull is that of an individual who died well below reproductive age.

Whole populations are not likely to become totally extinct. Even with the overrunning of other lands by Europeans in the last three centuries, Hottentots and Hopis, Polynesians and Pygmies, still survive. Although the last pure Tasmanian, a dark, woolly-haired woman called Truganini, died in 1877, and it is usually asserted that the Tasmanians have gone the way of the Great Auk, numerous mixed descendants of Tasmanians (mixed with Australian aborigines and Europeans) survive to this day on Cape Barren Island, Australia (Birdsell, 1948).

In tracing relations between fossils we need not imply direct ancestry. We merely refer to the taxonomic group to which the individual belongs, and arrows of relatedness should be taken to show connecting groups (that is, races, species, or even larger categories) rather than kinship between the former owners of individual skeletons. In the past some anthropologists have, on occasion, emphasized details in their fossil material that may very well represent nothing more than individual idiosyncracies. Isolated fossils must be judged in terms of the probable degree of variability that the members of a given group showed in respect to the particular bones in question. Of course, when only one specimen is available, the probable degree of variability can only be inferred from analogous features in other groups of man or other animals.

GENERAL REFERENCE

Simpson, G. G., 1949, *The Meaning of Evolution.* New Haven: Yale University Press. Part 2, "The Interpretation of Evolution," pages 123–279. Discusses the general principles of most interest to the anthropologist.

9 · Some Fossil Primates

Fossil Prosimii

The earliest primates known were prosimians who lived in the Paleocene and Eocene epochs. Most of their fossils have been found in North America and Europe, perhaps only because these are the most fully explored areas. In several instances the same families are known from specimens on both continents. Although we lack information establishing any of the half dozen or more distinct lines of these early primates as ancestors of any primates of the Miocene epoch or later, these early forms, in general, are quite similar to the Prosimii of today; some suggest affinities with Madagascar lemurs, or with the Asian and African lorises, and others with the tree shrews. To judge by the teeth, some seem to foretell the tarsier, and a few possess elongated bones of the foot—presumably used, as by the tarsier, for jumping.

Unfortunately, most fossils are known from incomplete skeletons, and for some of the Eocene and Paleocene forms we cannot say whether their gait was more like the hopping of the tarsier or the crawling of the slow loris. In many cases, only the teeth—usually a conservative feature slow to change during evolution—show that some of these earlier forms had closer affinities with one rather than with another modern form. In any case, there was apparently a radiation of prosimian types in the Paleocene and Eocene epochs, and some of these forms gave rise to all the later primates. *Progalago,* a Miocene forerunner of the galago; *Anagale,* a tree shrew from the Early Oligocene epoch of Mongolia; and a variety of lemurs from the Pleistocene period of Madagascar merely show that a few prosimians survived the Eocene. We know this anyway, for a modest number of species survive today. The main radiation seems to have been completed by the Oligocene period, except for the Pleistocene efflorescence in Madagascar, which gave rise to numerous lemurs, including one type larger than a pig.

Platyrrhine and Early Catarrhine Fossils

After the Eocene period, the evolution of primates seems to have been completely separate in the Old World and the New. The few fragmentary fossils of New World (platyrrhine, or flat-nosed) primates from the Miocene epoch of Argentina and Colombia are closely related to living New World monkeys and can have nothing to do with the radiation of the catarrhines—a term signifying that the nostrils point down and designating the Old World monkeys, the apes, and man.

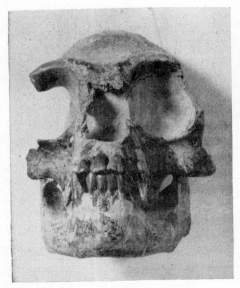

Fig. 9-1. (*a* and *b*). Pliopithecus skull from Neudorf, Czechoslovakia. Pliopithecus resembles the gibbons in its wide-set eyes relative to the breadth of the snout. (From Helmut Zapfe, "The Skeleton of *Pliopithecus* . . . ," *American Journal of Physical Anthropology*, 16(4), 1958. Courtesy of the author and the Journal.)

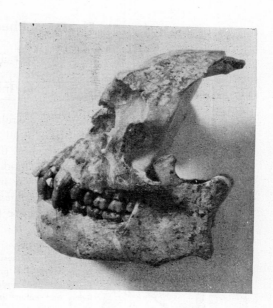

Fig. 9-1.(b).

In the Old World a few early catarrhine primate fossils are known. Several Oligocene specimens were found near Fayum, Egypt. One is a catarrhine frontal bone with orbits closed behind as in all later simia (Simons, 1959). Another, *Parapithecus* (from the Greek *para,* "next to," and *pithekos,* "ape"), from the little piece of jaw known of it, is considered by some authorities to be a primitive catarrhine, but probably not close to the human line of descent. Others doubt that it is a primate. A third, *Propliopithecus* (literally, "before" *Pliopithecus,* the "more apish"), in some ways foreshadows the gibbon and is probably not ancestral to any of the present-day monkeys.

Pliopithecus (Fig. 9-1) itself is known from some excellently preserved fossils from a deposit of early middle Miocene Age at Neudorf, Czechoslovakia. The teeth, narrow snout region, wide-set eyes, and some features of the collarbone and other long bones are gibbonlike or anthropoidal. Many other skeletal features, however, including the spinal column, upper limb, and general body proportions, are those of a monkey. Some of these features are distinctly primitive and can be most nearly matched in Old or New World monkeys or even Prosimians (Zapfe, 1958).

The Dryopithecinae

Until recently, virtually the only other Tertiary primate fossils discovered in the Old World were some apelike bits of bone from Europe and from the Siwalik Hills of India. They are usually grouped into a family or subfamily, the Dryopithecinae, although it seems highly doubtful that all were closely related to each other. Few long bones are known, and only bits of skull; but teeth are relatively numerous, and the lower molar teeth show the so-called Dryopithecus pattern also found—sometimes in modified form—in the gibbons, great apes, and man, but not in the monkeys.

The Dryopithecus pattern is an arrangement of the cusps, the little elevations on the biting surface of the teeth (Fig. 9-2). In its

Fig. 9-2. Dryopithecus pattern in a lower human molar tooth. The principal fissures form a "Y." This form and modifications of it are found in living and extinct pongids and hominids. (After Moorrees.)

simple form three cusps are arranged along the cheek side of the lower molars and two along the tongue side. The five cusps are separated by grooves (dentists call them fissures). In the Dryopithecus pattern three of these are especially deep and form a "Y." In contemporary apes the pattern is sometimes more or less obliterated by additional fine fissures; in man the cusps are sometimes smaller or fewer in number and the "Y" pattern of fissures may be modified to form a cross.

In recent years rich deposits of Miocene primates have been unearthed in East Africa. These are not too different from Dryopithecus in dental pattern but fall into two general groups. The smaller specimens, *Limnopithecus,* have long canine teeth, a trait they share with the gibbons. The gibbon is adept at arm-swinging locomotion and has extremely long arm bones. Limnopithecus and Pliopithecus have arm bones longer, relative to the bones of the leg, than such monkeys as the macaque and shorter than those of the apes. The forearm in Limnopithecus and Pliopithecus is intermediate in length, relative to the upper arm, between those of the gibbon and the remainder of the hominoids. These characteristics suggest that the forerunners of the gibbons had diverged from the quadrupedal monkeys and perhaps from the great apes by Miocene times.

Proconsul

The other East African Miocene primates, called Proconsul, are larger but vary greatly in size. The teeth range in size from smaller than those of a chimpanzee to larger than those of a gorilla. Fortunately, we have several long bones of *Proconsul africanus* and one nearly intact skull. The Proconsul skull was discovered in the steep side of a gully by Mrs. L. S. B. Leakey and extracted by her and her husband, a long-time archeologist and present curator of the museum in Nairobi, Kenya. The face of Proconsul is more constricted than that of an ape and resembles that of a monkey more closely, but the tooth pattern is definitely dryopithecine (that is, apelike and not monkeylike). The chin region of the jaw is heavy but lacks a *simian shelf* (Fig. 9-3) the buildup of bone on the

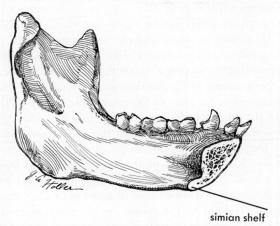

simian shelf

Fig. 9-3. Simian shelf on the inside of a half of a lower jaw bone (mandible). The simian shelf is a feature of the living monkeys and apes.

inside of the jaw which is found in both apes and monkeys today. This so-called simian shelf is also absent in the earlier Parapithecus from Egypt, in a later group of African fossil primates (the australopithecines), and in fossil and living man. The long bones of Proconsul do not show any specialization for brachiation, nor are they typical for ground-living primates such as the baboon. All we can really say of these limb bones is that they fit into the same pattern as the known fossil catarrhine long bones from Europe and, for that matter, those of living catarrhine monkeys.

Oreopithecus

Between the Miocene Proconsul and the Early Pleistocene South African man apes was a long time-interval of over ten million years. Some fossils recovered in coal mines of Tuscany in Italy help fill this gap in our knowledge. Most of the earlier reports concerning these so-called Oreopithecus specimens were written by scholars who never saw the specimens but relied on casts or previous descriptions. New explorations of the lignite coal fields of Tuscany reveal Oreopithecus deposits together with guide fossils of Early Pliocene date. Examination of all the Oreopithecus material now available shows several generalized hominoid features of the teeth and jaws, such as small canine teeth and short face, which may associate Oreopithecus more closely with man or the great apes than with monkeys (de Terra, 1956). Indeed, Hürzeler (1958), who has restudied the evidence, states that the teeth of Oreopithecus, although generalized or primitive, are *hominid* (of man's own family) rather than *pongid* (of the taxonomic family of the anthropoid apes). In other words, according to this view the teeth pertain to animals of the human rather than the ape taxonomic family as judged by their proportions, the shape of the lower premolars, and other details. Some features of the skull, jaws, and fragments of limb bones lead to the same conclusion, although the limb bones are generalized and resemble those of monkeys rather than those of apes or man. To add to the mosaic pattern represented by these fossils, the hand may have been long, a feature shared with arm-swinging apes. The vertebrae at the base of the spinal column are so large and strong, it is said, as not to exclude the possibility that

Oreopithecus could walk upright. If the foregoing assessment is valid, these remains may represent our first glimpse of a Tertiary hominid (Straus, 1957). On the other hand, adaptations to uprightness (whether for walking or swinging by the arms) could well be convergent, and, in classifying Oreopithecus, some authorities would place more emphasis on details of the molar teeth that clearly lack the Dryopithecus pattern of hominids and both early and recent pongids.

The Discovery of the Australo-pithecinae

In 1924 a South African quarryman working in a limestone deposit near a place called Taungs (or Taung, according to the official map) blasted out a small skull that he took to be manlike and so sent it to the anatomist at the University of Witwatersrand medical school, Professor Raymond Dart. Dart (1925) noted a number of resemblances to human skulls that are not shared by chimpanzees or gorillas. His views were immediately challenged in England by four authorities. Although today there is still a difference of opinion as to exactly how human these remains can be considered, it seems clear that in some respects they are surprisingly manlike. Dart called the species *Australopithecus africanus,* which means "southern ape from Africa" and has nothing to do with Australia.

Despite the unenthusiastic response of others to Dart's announcement, Dr. Robert Broom (1949), who had made an enviable reputation in paleontology by his study of the South African mammallike reptiles, went to see the skull, became convinced of its importance, and took up the search for more evidence. In the years since then Broom and Dart have found similar specimens in at least four other places in South Africa. The lime quarrying at Taung completely destroyed the deposit from which the first specimen had come (with the destruction of how much priceless fossil material we shall never know), but one of the men who had worked there knew enough about the fossils to recover specimens from a new quarry at Sterkfontein of which he was foreman. Two of Dart's students took Broom to the place, and the very next day he secured an australopithecine specimen. One day in 1938 the foreman sold

Broom a skull imbedded in limestone of a slightly different color. Broom wheedled from the foreman the name of the place from which he had taken it. The search led to a schoolboy, Gert Terblanche, still in class; before Broom was allowed to take the boy out, the principal had the scientist lecture on caves and bones. The boy took from his pocket "four of the most beautiful fossil teeth ever found in the world's history."

Broom had a knack for getting fossils. An American expedition, which had been hunting much of South Africa for likely sites and blasting tons of limestone from several deposits without success, once came to him. He selected for them a promising site at Swartkrans, only a mile from the Sterkfontein cave, and within a few days discovered the first of several enormous jaws (Fig. 9-4).

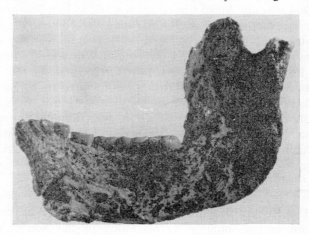

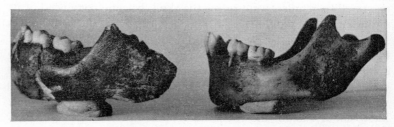

Fig. 9–4. *Top.* Huge australopithecine mandible from Swartkrans. *Bottom.* Mandible of a child from the same site (*left*) compared with that of a present-day American child (*right*). (From *Yearbook of Physical Anthropology,* 1949. Courtesy of John T. Robinson and Robert Broom.)

Classification of the Australopithecinae

Students of classification tend to be either "splitters," who emphasize differences, or "lumpers," who emphasize similarities. Broom, a notorious splitter, gave a designation to each new find and named three additional genera, even suggesting that they perhaps belong to different subfamilies. For our purpose, however, we may call the lot of them Australopithecus, a single genus, and reject the fine subdivisions. When Dart later came on new specimens at the limeworks cave at Makapan in Rhodesia, he considered these fossils to belong to the same genus as the Taung skull. All these fossils seem to come from similar limestone cave deposits of probably Early Pleistocene age. If we lump the specimens together, as I think we are justified in doing, we can compare them as a group with other primates.

So long as there is disagreement about the relationships (hence about the correct scientific names) of these fossils, we may do well to refer to them by the names of the places where they were found.

Place	Name
Taung (or Taungs)	*Australopithecus africanus*, Dart
Makapan	*Australopithecus prometheus*, Dart
Sterkfontein	*Plesianthropus transvaalensis*, Broom
Kromdraai	*Paranthropus robustus*, Broom
Swartkrans	*Paranthropus crassidens*, Broom

John Robinson (1954), Broom's successor at the Transvaal Museum in Pretoria, South Africa, has recently reexamined the taxonomy and groups the first three of these in one species (Fig. 9-5) and the last two in another (Fig. 9-6).

The Antiquity of the Australopithecinae

All five sites were in limestone; in fact, it was the commercial quarrying for limestone that led to the original discovery. The fossil bones of which the caves were full had become cemented together with lime to form a mass of rock and bone called *breccia*. Some of the fossils have come from breccia thrown aside by quarrymen, for

Fig. 9-5. Australopithecine skull of the smaller variety from Sterkfontein. The skull vault is higher and more rounded behind, but little if any bigger than that of a chimpanzee or gorilla. (From *Yearbook of Physical Anthropology*, 1949. Courtesy of John T. Robinson and Robert Broom.)

it was their job to obtain as clean and undisturbed a limestone as possible; others have been blasted from the cemented deposits. In no case is the exact stratigraphy known. The best evidence concerning the age of the deposits is therefore found in the associated fossil fauna. In general the particular association of extinct and non-extinct types is equated with the latter part of what in Europe is called Villafranchian. During this stage, modern types of horse and baboon were evolving, but saber-toothed tigers and many other forms now extinct persisted. The Villafranchian represents, according to the more usual view, the beginning of the Pleistocene epoch. Because the Villafranchian antedates the continental glaciations and because the other fossil animals found together with the australopithecines are a Villafranchian assemblage, I would give a date of roughly a million years to the australopithecines. Some experts emphasize the extinct fossil forms and have placed the australopithecines a little earlier; others, emphasizing the modern forms, would place the final extinction of the australopithecines a little

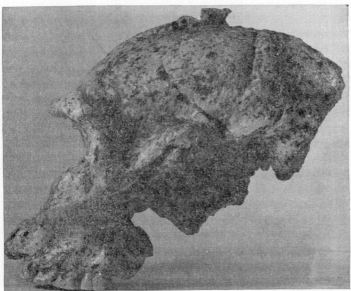

Fig. 9-6. Australopithecine skulls of the larger variety from Swartkrans. The top skull manifests rugged features and a very low forehead. The bottom one has a sagittal crest, the protrusion of bone at the top. (From *Yearbook of Physical Anthropology,* 1949. Courtesy of John T. Robinson and Robert Broom.)

CLASSIFICATION OF THE AUSTRALOPITHECINAE ◆ 81

later. Actually, they may have lived for some time, according to a detailed study of the probable climate based on the shape of grains of sand. The Sterkfontein and Taung sites seem early, the limeworks cave at Makapan slightly later, and the Swartkrans and finally the Kromdraai site latest (Howell, 1955).

Skulls and Jaws of the Australopithecinae

Swartkrans and Kromdraai yielded the big-jawed form. The great size of these jaws, the wear of the teeth, and the relative lack of good meat animals represented by the accompanying fossil bones suggest a vegetarian diet. By contrast, the earlier, smaller form is found at Makapan, in association with the broken bones of numerous ruminants. The remains from all five sites include a number of skulls, several of which are well preserved and nearly intact; several mandibles (jaw bones); numerous adult and deciduous ("baby") teeth; and a number of pieces of other bones, including the larger parts of several hip bones and the ends of some limb bones.

The most notable feature of the various skulls of the Australopithecinae is that they combine large jaws with relatively small skulls. The skull capacity of normal human beings ranges from less than a liter (hence just under a quart) to two and one-half liters. The best preserved skulls of the Australopithecinae have a capacity of 0.4 or 0.5 liter. This means that the brains were about the size of those of gorillas and chimpanzees and smaller than those of normal men and women. Since a liter is just over a quart, on the basis of brain content these creatures might well be called "pint sized." On the basis of several of the less well-measured specimens, where the volume cannot accurately be measured, and by extrapolating to probable adult dimensions from juvenile skulls (and even to large male dimensions from putative females) Broom and others have ascribed to the Australopithecinae skull a volume that may reach 0.6, 0.7, or even 0.8 liter. However, there is no direct evidence for assuming that australopithecine brains were larger than those of great apes.

Another apelike feature of the skull is the presence in some specimens (Fig. 9-6b) from Swartkrans of a raised crest along the sagittal suture that marks the midline of the vertex or dome of the

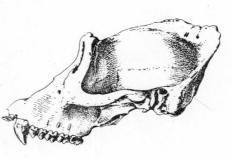

Fig. 9-7. A male gorilla skull. The sagittal crest of bone at the top relates to powerful chewing muscles. In contrast with the australopithecine skull (Fig. 9-6), the cresting in the gorilla extends to the back (occiput). The large overlapping canine teeth and associated gap (diastema) seen in the gorilla are lacking in the australopithecines. (From A. H. Schultz, *American Journal of Physical Anthropology, 5*(5), 1947. Courtesy of the author and the Journal.)

skull. The sagittal crest occurs in male gorillas (Fig. 9-7) and chimpanzees and other animals with powerful temporal muscles (that is, chewing muscles that cover the temple and side of the head), but does not occur in man, although the lines of attachment of the muscles in Eskimos sometimes nearly produce one.

The australopithecine teeth, too, give interesting evidence and have been the subject of some recent controversy. The most striking feature is that the canine teeth, although pointed, are not as long as in virtually all primates except man. The premolar teeth are also unlike those of the great apes; they are not shaped for scissorlike action but meet end to end, as in man. The order of eruption of the permanent teeth is said to be more like that of man than that of the apes. Too much emphasis should not be placed on this resemblance, however, because there are wide variations in the order in both man and apes. The front teeth are small, as in man, while the back teeth are large, as in apes. The upper teeth are in a continuous row unbroken by the diastema, the gap that is always found above the large simian type of lower canine tooth. Furthermore, the wear of the teeth tends to be even, and this is said to correspond to a form of the jaw joint similar to man's. This feature is variable in apes, however, and flat wear occurs in an occasional chimpanzee. Several of the jaws, both upper and lower, show single holes for blood vessels and nerves, as in man, but again it must be stressed that these features are variable in both man and apes. These holes are called mental and infraorbital foramina and occur in the lower and upper jaw respectively (Fig. 9-8).

CLASSIFICATION OF THE AUSTRALOPITHECINAE ◆ 83

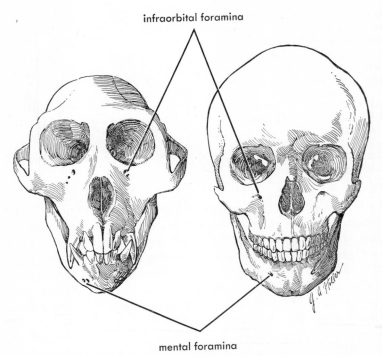

infraorbital foramina

mental foramina

Fig. 9-8. Infraorbital and mental foramina, usually single in modern man (*right*), frequently multiple in other primates such as the macaque monkey (*left*).

"Telanthropus"

One jaw from Swartkrans especially seems to show human affinities; the teeth are much smaller, and there is even, possibly, an incipient chin. Some other fragments and teeth have been classed with this jaw as a new manlike genus, "Telanthropus" (Fig. 9-9). These remains may not belong to the australopithecine group, but in the present state of our knowledge—or ignorance—it seems more reasonable to include them with the others. They do not seem significantly different from the smaller, Sterkfontein, variety.

The Olduvai Discovery

Dr. L. S. B. Leakey and his wife have been responsible for several notable discoveries bearing on human origins. It is probably

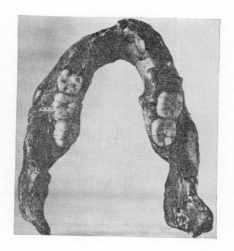

Fig. 9-9. "Telanthropus" mandible, an australopithecine mandible from Swartkrans that is in some ways rather human and fits in better with the smaller Sterkfontein and Makapan australopithecines than with the big mandibles from Swartkrans. (From *Yearbook of Physical Anthropology*, 1949, Courtesy of John T. Robinson and Robert Broom.)

no accident that Dart, Broom, and Leakey have been responsible for a whole series of discoveries. Each of these scholars learned how to look, each went to Africa and maintained the search for decades, and each has transmitted his enthusiasm to those around him and has hence found able assistants in the field.

In 1959 the Leakeys were working in Olduvai Gorge, where crude stone tools occur and one enormous primate tooth had earlier been found. On July 17, Mrs. Leakey was working on an excavation in a cliff while her husband, who was ill, remained in camp. She was on the point of joining him there when she saw a small fragment of bone with skull texture. She then located three teeth that looked human and, after marking the spot so she could find it again, hurried to tell her husband. As he puts it: "My sickness vanished like magic." He hurried to the spot, took photographs of the teeth still in place in the ground, and then uncovered a much broken but nearly complete fossil skull. This skull was found on the actual living floor occupied by the users of crude stone choppers and stone flakes of the earliest stone-age culture of Africa, the Oldowan of Early Pleistocene date. The skull may well have belonged to a member of the group who knocked chips and flakes off stones in order to shape more useful tools. Animal bones found on the floor are those of small animals. It appears that big-game hunting was not practiced there, although the bones of large animals at other sites have been considered by some as the remains of Australopithecus meals.

The preliminary description and photographs (Leakey, 1959) are of a skull related in a general way to the more robust of the australopithecines, and I see no reason for the creation of the new generic name that was given to it—Zinjanthropus. The back teeth are enormous, even larger than those of Paranthropus, but the front teeth are small and "human." The palate is highly arched. The rest of the skull is similar to those of the australopithecines in size, but it has some special features. There is a sagittal crest as in Paranthropus and the great apes. There is also an occipital crest for the attachment of neck muscles, but it is quite different from that of gorillas and is associated with a large mastoid process behind the ear (Fig. 9-10), such as is seen in man. Some of the features and the evidence of the tools lead me to assume that such a being had a well-developed bipedal stance. The shin bone (tibia) found with the skull has not been described in detail. In any case one would need further leg and hip bones to be sure of the posture.

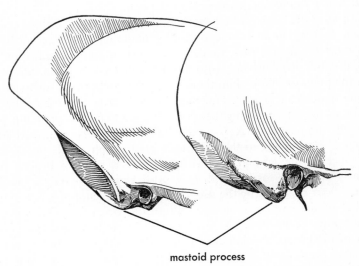

mastoid process

Fig. 9-10. The mastoid process, little if at all developed in the gorilla (*left*), always present—but variable in size—in man (*right*).

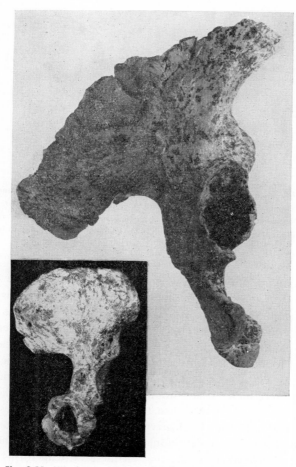

Fig. 9-11. Hip bones of australopithecines (photographed at different scales). The upper part (ilium) is splayed out, but the lower part (ischium) is somewhat elongated. (From *Yearbook of Physical Anthropology,* 1949. Courtesy of John T. Robinson and Robert Broom.)

The Hip Bones of the Australopithecinae

Hip bones (*pelves*) of man and apes are very different, and here the australopithecine specimens (Fig. 9-11) show close resemblance to man—although it is doubtful that the australopithecines had a

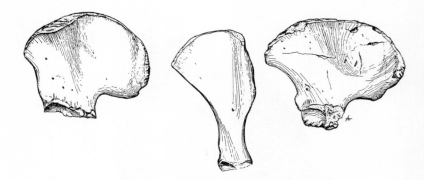

Fig. 9-12. The upper part of the hip bone (ilium) of, *left to right,* young human (Bushman), chimpanzee, and australopithecine (from Makapan). The ilium of the australopithecines is essentially human in form. (From R. A. Dart, *American Journal of Physical Anthropology,* 7(307), 1949. Courtesy of the author and the Journal.)

fully human upright posture. The upper part (ilium) is splayed out, as in modern man, and the ape's elongation of the pelvis is not marked (Fig. 9-12). One specimen in particular has some simian characteristics in the lower part (ischium) that suggest bent-knee running, but in general the pelves are so human that, had they been found alone, most anatomists would have ascribed them to man. As a matter of fact, some persons do just that and claim that there were men (Telanthropus) and apes (australopithecines) in the same region at the same time. However, since these finds exhibit really only one variable type of pelvis and one general type of skull and one type of dentition, I prefer to believe that there is a connection between them and that all these African forms should be assumed to be related to each other until evidence to the contrary suggests that we consider them separately. If there was just one type of hominid present, the recent evidence of deliberately worked stone tools in the deposits and the older suggestions concerning bone tools can point only to the australopithecines as the tool makers. Upright stance would permit simultaneous holding of tools in the hands while running or walking. This stance would be favored by changes in the pelvis, of the kind seen in the australopithecines (Fig. 9-13).

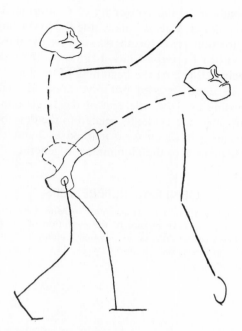

Fig. 9-13. The differences in posture between australopithecine (*left*) and great ape (*right*) that are believed
to be associated with the differences in the ilium (see Fig. 9-
12).

The Significance of the Australopithecinae for Human Evolution

We should not minimize the variation, however. It seems greater
than in most species, greater even than that of modern man. This
variability adds to the probability that the Australopithecinae we e
a radiating group. We think of them as radiating rather than evolving in a line because the apparently earlier specimens appear more
man-like than the later ones, except in brain size. The later ones had
large back teeth associated with marked development of those bony
areas of the skull and jaws to which the chewing muscles attach.
Although these muscles must have been huge, some anatomists
argue from the shape of the bony attachments that their disposition
was quite different from that in the gorilla.

In summarizing our knowledge of the Australopithecinae we
should note the view set forth in 1951 in a brief article by Professor

Sherwood Washburn of the University of California. He contends that certain functional systems—including the lower limb—evolved in a human direction prior to others, such as the masticatory apparatus. Sir Wilfrid Le Gros Clark (1955, p. 161) describes the Australopithecinae thus: At the beginning of the Pleistocene epoch in South Africa there "existed primitive hominids with a cranial capacity exceeding by very little that of the large anthropoid apes but with a limb structure evidently related to the development of an erect posture and gait which is so marked a characteristic of the evolutionary sequences of the Hominidae in general."

GENERAL REFERENCES

Clark, W. E. Le Gros, 1960, *The Antecedents of Man.* Chicago: Quadrangle Books. A comprehensive picture of the evolution of the primate order.
———, 1955, *The Fossil Evidence for Human Evolution.* Chicago: University of Chicago Press. See Chapter 4, pages 113–161, for an account of the australopithecines.

10 · Java Man and Peking Man

Lomo sapien

The Original Java Man, *Pithecanthropus erectus*

In 1863, Thomas Huxley, who had been one of the first vocal defendants of Darwin's thesis of natural selection, published his most renowned work on the subject, *Evidence as to Man's Place in Nature*. Huxley showed that man is similar to the great apes, that he is nearer to the apes than, for example, the apes are to dogs. In 1871 Darwin himself attempted an explanation of how this *Descent of Man* could have come about through selection of secondary sexual characteristics.

The present concern, however, is with the history of discovery of direct evidences of human evolution. Although it is an extreme simplification, we can conceive of human evolution since the last common ancestor of anthropoids and man as having occurred in four stages: (1) manlike apes, (2) apelike men, (3) primitive species of man, and (4) fossil types of man, members of our species, *Homo sapiens*. A skeleton belonging to a primitive species of man, stage (3), was discovered in 1856 in a ravine called Neanderthal in Prussia (see Chapter 11). By 1868 the fossil evidences of stage (4), Cro-Magnon man, had been described. The first two stages were considered to be "missing links"—an erroneous way of viewing the continuous flow of evolution, but one that persists even today when all the originally conceived "links" are reasonably well represented by actual fossil remains. No evidences of anything that could be called a man ape, the first stage, were to turn up until Dart's discovery of Australopithecus in 1924. In 1891 and 1892, during a deliberate search on the island of Java for "the missing link," the ape man of the second stage, Dr. Eugene Dubois found a fossil human thigh bone (femur), some fossilized teeth, and a skull cap. Relatively little can be said of the teeth, which are much worn. The femur, though old and fossilized, looks like that of modern man. The skull cap, however, is intermediate between those of man and the apes in size and shape. It is low and narrow, especially just behind the forehead region, and there is a horizontal ridge of bone (supraorbital torus) extending over both eye sockets. The brain, or more exactly the cranial cavity, is small by human standards, but far exceeds in size that of any known ape. Dubois gave this fossil the name he had been saving, *Pithecanthropus erectus,* the erect ape man (Fig. 10-1).

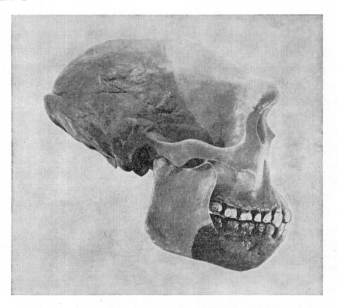

Fig. 10-1. The skull of Java man, *Pithecanthropus.* The light parts represent reconstruction by Franz Weidenreich on the basis of other specimens and interpolation. The brain case is low and small by modern human standards. There are two moundlike bars of bone: a supraorbital torus in front over the eye sockets, and an occipital torus in back. There is a mastoid process, a human characteristic, but no chin. (Courtesy of The American Museum of Natural History.)

Our knowledge of Pithecanthropus has been greatly expanded by the discovery of additional specimens in Java in the years just prior to World War II. G. H. R. von Koenigswald, the paleontologist responsible for finding them, hid some fossil teeth in a milk bottle and gave other fossils to friends for safe keeping when the Japanese invaded Java and he was interned for four years. The specimens remained little known until the end of the war when descriptions were published and von Koenigswald brought the specimens to the American Museum of Natural History in New York to study. All of these, like the original finds, had turned up in the walls of gullies cut in Pleistocene alluvial gravel deposits along rivers. Here Pithecanthropus must have died, out in the open, some half million years ago. No evidence of any tools has been found with his remains. With these and subsequent finds the simple four-stage scheme becomes inadequate: We begin to see human evolution for what it is, a complex network of living forms in which changes, at one time slow, at another surprisingly rapid, occur now in one, now in another feature. The whole makes the evolutionary patterns in time and space wherein variety is the norm and type an abstraction.

Of the Pithecanthropus specimens recovered by von Koenigswald in Java, two further skulls conform closely with the first one found by Dubois. They are thick, and the cranial capacities of all three skulls range from approximately 0.8 to about 0.9 liter. The child's skull from Modjokerto holds about 0.7 liter but might have reached a liter had its possessor lived to adulthood. The new specimens add important information about the occiput, the bone at the back of the skull. In Pithecanthropus it is shelved for a large attachment of the neck muscles and ends in a moundlike prominence, and occipital torus. There is also a mastoid process, the bony bump you can feel just behind the lower part of your ear. This is a human characteristic sometimes present in rudimentary form in adult gorillas. It is never seen in the young of any living nonhuman primate, but is present in the Modjokerto youth.

Among von Koenigswald's material there is also a lower jaw and, with one of the skulls, an upper jaw. Both jaws are large and robust.

The teeth are large. The elevations on the biting surfaces, the cusps, are of human pattern; where the cusps are worn off, there are signs of a characteristic human type of wear. The canine teeth overlap somewhat, the lower meeting a small gap (diastema) between the upper canine and lateral incisor teeth in at least one instance. Such a diastema of larger size is frequent in modern apes but, as we have already noted, absent in the australopithecines as well as in modern man. In the lower jaw there is no chin, and the mental foramen—as in most apes—is multiple. Nevertheless, the jaws are definitely more human than apelike in size and proportions and in the teeth they carry.

Meganthropus

In addition to these specimens von Koenigswald recovered a jaw fragment of truly massive proportions from which he calls the specimen *Meganthropus*, "large man." It has larger teeth than the other specimens but they are of the same general shape and pattern. Dr. Franz Weidenreich, a distinguished anthropologist of whom we shall hear again in connection with Peking man, believed that man's forebears were gigantic and that there was a succession from Meganthropus to *Pithecanthropus erectus*, with all of these belonging to the same genus. Others have classed Meganthropus separately or compared it with the australopithecines. (Similarly, some have compared "Telanthropus" of the australopithecine deposits with Pithecanthropus.) A second small fragment of mandible, from the same place, seems to me hardly less massive than the first, but more cautious authorities have so far suspended judgment on it.

The Antiquity of Pithecanthropus

The Pithecanthropus fossils come from two different strata of the Early or Middle Pleistocene of Java. The majority of the specimens, including the original finds, come from the Trinil deposits that were formerly considered Early Pleistocene but are more probably Middle Pleistocene in date. The other stratum, called Djetis—which yielded the Modjokerto infant skull, the Meganthropus jaw, and the other jaw bones—is earlier, and the fossils in it may therefore have been contemporary with Australopithecus. Even if true, this fact would not of itself rule out Australopithecus-like ancestors for Pithecanthropus (and modern man) but, if the dates are confirmed, it would lead us to seek earlier australopithecines as the actual ancestors. At one time there was a question as to whether so modern a type of bone as the femur could belong with the skull. There now seems no reason why the evolution of the lower limb should not have preceded expansion of the brain, and a recent study of the fluorine content of the femur and of other fossil human thigh bones from Java, brought to Holland by Dubois, yields a date contemporary with that of fossil animal bones from the Trinil Pleistocene deposits of Java.

Peking Man

In 1921, while only the original Pithecanthropus remains were known, and these unassociated with any evidence of tools, J. G. Anderson, a Swedish geologist working in North China, noticed chips of quartz—apparently not native to the place—in the limestone filling of a Pleistocene cave at the town of Choukoutien, some 30 miles west of Peking. The implication was that the quartz must have been brought by prehistoric men. Excavations were begun and soon revealed a human tooth, the first of a number of finds. The American anatomist Davidson Black (1927), who was then teaching at a Chinese medical school, has always been given much credit for recognizing that the single tooth was human and that it belonged to a distinct genus of man, which he called *Sinanthropus pekinensis* (Fig. 10-2). Actually, compared with the other teeth later unearthed, this one is rather atypical, and the granting of a new name may have been premature—even if one were to concede a new human genus on the basis of the subsequent material. Peking man turns out to be very similar to Java man; perhaps he is best thought of as a member of the same species or of a similar one, *Pithecanthropus pekinensis*.

Shortly after describing the first of the remains, Davidson Black died. At the same time, Dr. Franz Weidenreich was compelled to leave Germany, where the Nazis had come to power. Weidenreich

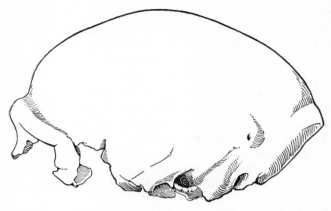

Fig. 10-2. One of the skulls of Peking man. It is much like that of Java man (Fig. 10-1), but the brain case is larger. (After Weidenreich.)

(1936, 1937, 1941, 1943) went to China and examined and described the various finds of Peking man in four monographs (on the lower jaws, teeth, long bones, and skull respectively) and in numerous shorter reports. (Incidentally, the word "man" is used in such terms as "Peking man" without implying that the bones are those of males. In most cases it is impossible to be sure of the sex of an individual from partial bony remains.) We are fortunate to have Weidenreich's reports and excellent casts of some of the specimens of Peking man because, in the first days of the war between the United States and Japan, all the original specimens were lost. They had been put in charge of a United States Marine officer who, after his war-long internment by the Japanese, remembered only that the old bones had been put on a train from Peking to Tientsin. That is the last anyone knows of them. They may have been on a ship that was sunk, or they may never have reached the seaport. The group contained several skulls, over a dozen mandibles, and numerous teeth besides fragments of other bones. All that remain today are five teeth, two fragments of limb bones, and a mandible subsequently found by Chinese scientists (Woo, 1956; Woo and Chao, 1959), and two teeth later turned up in a collection of fossil animal bones from the site, which had been stored at the University of Uppsala, Sweden.

Relationship of Peking Man to Modern Mongoloids

Some of the skulls of Peking man are of fully human size, the capacity ranging from .9 to 1.3 liters. They are much like those of Java man in other ways, notably in having marked bony bulges fore and aft (supraorbital and occipital tori). The skulls are wide at the base, and at the top they narrow to a ridge. It is not the elevated sagittal crest of gorilla and some of the australopithecines, built up when the two temporal muscles meet each other at the midline of the top of the skull, but merely a ridge that gives the skull a gabled rooflike appearance. The face protrudes, and the nose is broad. The teeth, like those of *Pithecanthropus erectus,* are large and set in large jaws. There is no chin. The mental foramen is always multiple.

Weidenreich has called attention to a few features that Peking man shared with modern Mongoloid peoples including the present-day Chinese. The midline ridge, already referred to, is one of these. There is also an overgrowth of the bone of the lower jaw behind the canine teeth—the so-called mandibular torus (Fig. 10-3), common in Eskimos and also occurring occasionally in Europeans and others. The molar teeth have large pulp cavities (*taurodont*—that is, "teeth

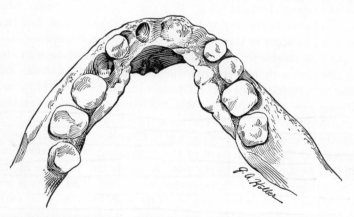

Fig. 10-3. Mandibular torus on the inside of each side of a modern human mandible. Such bony protuberances, common in Eskimos and some other peoples, occur in Peking man. (After Moorrees.)

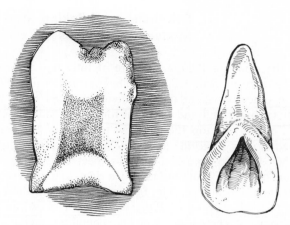

Fig. 10-4 (*left*). Taurodont molar with large, dark, rectangular pulp cavity, as seen in an x-ray. (After Abbie.) Fig. 10-5 (right). Shovel-shaped upper incisor, concave toward the tongue, a form especially frequent and pronounced in Mongoloid peoples and found also in Peking man. (After Moorrees and Tratman.)

like a bull's"), a feature rare in primates but pronounced especially in Neanderthal man and, to some extent, in some modern Mongoloid peoples (Fig. 10-4). The front teeth are concave behind. These "shovel-shaped" incisors (Fig. 10-5) are present in most Mongoloid individuals (including East Asians, Eskimos, and American Indians) and occur in less pronounced form when Europeans manifest the trait. Weidenreich concluded that, although these traits suggest affinities with modern man in the same part of Asia, these would not preclude ancestral relations with modern man in general. The great time span (since the Middle Pleistocene) and the presence of non-Mongoloid man in the same place in the meanwhile (as attested by the three skulls of the Upper Cave at Choukoutien) make a direct and separate descent of the Mongoloids from Peking man unlikely. In any case, Peking man is much less like the modern Chinese than he is like *Pithecanthropus erectus*. The latter is a bit more primitive not only by reason of its probably somewhat earlier date, but also in respect to a few features: smaller skull, lower and flatter in the forehead region, and larger jaws, at least one of which shows the gap for overlap of the canine teeth.

GENERAL REFERENCE

Weidenreich, F., 1946, *Apes, Giants and Men*. Chicago: University of Chicago Press. Weidenreich's distinctive views on human evolution are simply presented in this work. Chapter 3 (pp. 47–66) describes some of the fossils from Java and China.

11 · Neanderthal and Other Fossil Men

Neanderthal Man

Neanderthal man is that well-known and surprisingly consistent form of man represented by skeletons found in a wide variety of places, in caves of the Last Glaciation. We take him up now simply because abundant material is available, and not because he has a better claim to being one of our ancestors than do several other fossil forms. Even if he is considered a side branch, however, Neanderthal man clearly belongs to the genus *Homo* and is the best known reference type for nonsapiens man. "Neanderthal" is the name of the valley near Dusseldorf, Germany, where the first specimen was found. Other skulls of the type, nearly as much alike as members of the same family, have been unearthed elsewhere in Germany, and in France (Fig. 11-1), Belgium, Gibraltar, and Italy (Fig. 11-2). Somewhat less typical specimens have been found in Yugoslavia, Germany, Czechoslovakia, Italy, North Africa, Palestine, and as far away as Uzbekistan in Central Asia and Kwangtung Province in China.

First, it may be well to characterize the West European type as represented by the almost complete skeleton from La Chapelle-Aux-Saints, France, and the skulls from the La Ferrassie, France, and Monte Circeo, Italy. The skull has a capacity of over 1.6 liters, large even for modern man. The skull size has led to the assertion that Neanderthal man exceeds modern man in the volume of his brain;

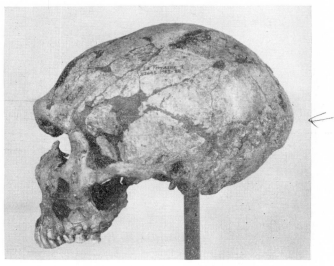

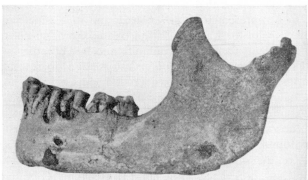

Fig. 11-1. Skull from La Ferrassie, France; a typical Neanderthal specimen with frontal torus and low vault. (Photograph, collection of Museé de l'Homme. Courtesy of the Wenner-Gren Foundation for Anthropological Research.)

taking all specimens into account, however, Neanderthal skulls range down to about 1.3 liters, duplicating the range of the modern European populations. The Neanderthal skull is flattened down and has a large mound-shaped frontal torus over the orbits (the bony cavities that contain the eyes). At the back of the head there is a backward extension of the occiput and an occipital torus. The foramen

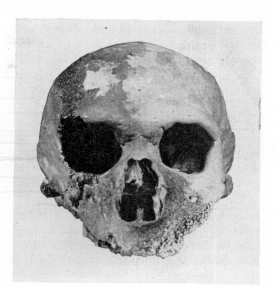

Fig. 11-2. Skull from Monte Circeo, Italy; a Neanderthal specimen closely similar to that of La Ferrassie (Fig. 11-1). (Courtesy of Sergio Sergi.)

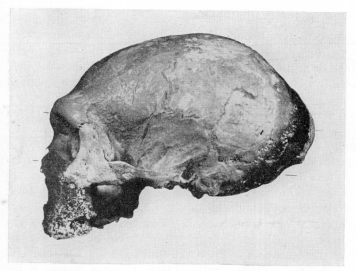

magnum, the hole in the skull through which the spinal cord connects with the brain, is well back on the skull base; this is associated with long single spines on the vertebrae of the neck—a sign of more powerful back muscles than are found in modern man. The position of the foramen magnum and evidence concerning the upper back imply that the head was thrust forward rather than being balanced erect on top of the vertebrae of the neck. The face is long and wide, with jutting jaws (*prognathism*). By contrast, modern men with large brow ridges, notably Australian aborigines, usually have short faces. Neanderthal teeth are large and set in large jaws, but the teeth are completely human. As already noted, however, the pulp cavities of the molars are exceptionally deep (taurodont) in a way rarely found in modern man. The chin is absent, and the jaws are robust with a wide area for attachment of the chewing muscles.

The Neanderthal face is set forward on the skull so that the angle at the base of the skull is very obtuse. In modern men, including those with low, flattened skulls, this angle is somewhat smaller. In fact, the higher the human head the more likely that the short radius of curvature of the back of the crown will be accompanied by a small basal angle, as if the whole back of the skull were pushed up under the front part.

Reconstruction of Neanderthal Man

Reconstructions of Neanderthal man usually picture him as standing stooped forward with knees bent. The basis for this was the position of the foramen magnum, the angle at the base of the skull, and especially the rugged limb bones with bent shafts and enlarged joints. The bowed shaft of the bones of the thigh and leg and the direction of the joints of the bones of the leg and foot have suggested to some authors a characteristic and more apelike bent-knee gait. It should be kept in mind that the description of the limbs of Neanderthal man is based largely on the single specimen from La Chapelle-Aux-Saints (although other fragments of limb bones are known). We know, however, that five fossil thigh bones from Java, parts of seven from Peking man, and, as we shall see, the limb bones of Solo man, Rhodesian man, and the Palestine fossils are of modern human type. Straus and Cave (1957), among others, have reexamined the limb bones of the skeleton from La Chapelle and conclude that the individual suffered from a severe disease of the joints. Although the skeleton presents some distinctive features, none of these contradict the possibility of a human upright posture as normal as is seen in modern man with similar arthritis.

Another feature of the attempted reconstructions of Neanderthal man is the invariable aspect of copious straight or wavy black hair. We have, of course, no evidence whatever concerning hair, except that Neanderthal man lived at the height of the Last Glaciation, and that some of his contemporaries, the woolly rhinoceros and the woolly mammoth, had plenty of hair. Hairy or not, Neanderthal man was probably well protected by the hair of his contemporaries— that is, the fur of animals. Bones of many species are found together with Neanderthal man's stone tools, which are of characteristic forms collectively referred to as the "Mousterian Industry." One of the common types of flint tool is of a shape that would serve well for scraping as in preparing pelts. Neanderthal man's own bones, those of his prey, his stone tools, and ashes from his hearths are all found together in limestone caves and grottos of Europe. From them we can infer a rugged hunting way of life and a society of small family groups. All of the known skulls that can be dated come from deposits of the Last Interglacial or the first phase of the Last Glaciation (about 115,000 years ago according to the astronomical theory). Although the characteristic Mousterian tools are found in later deposits, there is no direct evidence that Neanderthal man survived, and in one site in Russia late Mousterian tools are associated with bones of modern type man.

Early Man from Palestine and Iraq

To describe fossil specimens somewhat like Neanderthal but different, scholars have added the suffix "-oid" meaning "-like." Hence, Neanderthaloid means Neanderthal-like just as anthropoid, the name for the great apes, is the "-oid" compound of the Greek root for man, "anthrop." The term "anthropoid" does not include man, and "Neanderthaloid" does not include the true Neanderthal man. A considerable variety of fossil specimens have been found that resemble Neanderthal man only in part and are thus classed as Neanderthaloid. These come not from Western Europe but from Eastern Europe, North Africa, and Western Asia.

Among the most interesting specimens are the remains from Mount Carmel in Palestine. These were excavated between 1929 and 1934 from two caves (Tabūn and Skhūl) by members of a joint British and American expedition under the direction of the distinguished British archeologist Dr. Dorothy Garrod. The two cave deposits are believed to be of about the same antiquity (McCown and Keith, 1939). Zeuner (1958), however, believes that the Tabūn skull belongs late in the Last Interglacial while the Skhūl skeletons are a bit later and date to the beginning of the first phase of the Last Glaciation. The best preserved Tabūn skull is slightly less robust than those of typical European Neanderthalians but, like them, lacks a chin and has very prominent bony ridges above the eyes. If this had been the only specimen found, it would probably have been called Neanderthal. In fact, a fragment previously found in Palestine at the northeastern end of the Sea of Galilee was so classified.

Some of the Skhūl specimens—virtually as ancient—are more like modern man. They have a forehead that, although it is marked with large brow ridges, is rounded and also high. These ridges, unlike those of the West European Neanderthalians, are divided in the middle as in contemporary men who have prominent brow ridges (especially some Europeans and aboriginal Australians). In the Skhūl specimens the back of the skull is rounded, the facial skeleton is more delicate, and there is a definite chin. The long bones are not appreciably different from those of modern man.

Six hundred miles to the north and east of Mount Carmel is a cave in the Shanidar Valley of northern Iraq; here an American expedition led by Ralph Solecki of the Smithsonian Institution has recently discovered human skeletons in association with Mousterian culture (Anon., 1957). By C^{14} tests the stratum is shown to be over some 50,000 years old, but it is believed that the skeletons are more recent than those from Mount Carmel in Palestine. This poses an interesting problem, since the Shanidar man, with a long face and small mastoid processes, is more typically Neanderthalian. The skull is comparable to those of Western European Neanderthal man except for a few details such as separate brow ridges.

If the man from the Shanidar Cave and the Neanderthal man of Europe are more recent than the Neanderthaloids of the Skhūl cave, the latter would seem to have a better claim to be regarded as our evolving ancestors.

The eastern end of the Mediterranean would have provided a more hospitable climate for development of the species than would Ice

Age Europe. However, as we shall note later, some anthropologists believe that modern man had already developed at an earlier period. In either case, the evidence is mounting that _Homo sapiens_ and _Homo neanderthalensis_ were at one time living side by side. Some anthropologists therefore find it easy to explain the Mount Carmel enigma as the result of hybridization—a notion that rests in part on a false premise. At the time it was put forward, there was a widespread idea that hybrid populations are more variable than isolated populations, and there certainly is a range of types at Mount Carmel. In the meanwhile, it has become clear that racially composite groups are no more variable than unmixed peoples. Mulattos, for example, range from light to dark but show no more tendency to vary in skin color and other respects than do Negroes or Whites.

Some Other Neanderthaloids

During 1948 excavations in a cave at Haua Fteah in Cyranaica in North Africa, Charles McBurney (1953) found a jaw fragment in the lowest and oldest layers that turns out to be much like the Mount Carmel specimens. Using the radioactive carbon method the U.S. Geological Survey has dated charcoal with which it was found at over 34,000 years.

One of the most interesting Neanderthaloid specimens is the Steinheim skull found in a place by that name in Germany in 1933. This skull was found in the same gravel deposits as extinct warm-climate animals and is hence ascribed to one of the warm interglacial periods antedating the Last Glaciation. It is often considered to belong to the great Penultimate Interglacial. No stone tools were found with it. The skull itself is low, a Neanderthal feature, and exhibits massive brow ridges (though these have been described by some as of the type occasionally found in man today). Although the skull is small, the forehead is somewhat rounded, and so is the occiput. Furthermore, the region around the ear does not differ greatly from that of modern man.

Another skull from Germany was excavated at Ehringsdorf near Weimar in 1925 and described by Weidenreich (1927) while he still lived in Germany. The skull conforms well with that from Steinheim. It was found in a stratified deposit overlying a river terrace. From the geology and from the associated fossils, it seems probable that Ehringsdorf man lived during the last part of the Last Interglacial. The stone tools are said to be more primitive than those of West European Neanderthal man. The skull itself is fragmentary, but the full frontal region and well-developed mastoid process of modern type are, as in the Steinheim man, associated with large brow ridges.

Quite recently a fossil skull has been found in Mapa in Kwantung, China, which, to judge from a preliminary description and photographs (Woo and Peng, 1959), is similar enough to the European Neanderthal specimens to be classed as Neanderthaloid. The skull fragment was found together with fossil animal types of the end of Middle or the beginning of Late Pleistocene times. The skull vault is as low as that of some Neanderthal skulls. The frontal torus resembles that of Neanderthal man in some respects and that of Solo man (see below) in others. The orbits are rounded as in Neanderthal man. This specimen is so far the only one of the kind from anywhere in the Far East.

Another Fossil Type from Java, Solo Man

In other parts of the world a number of skulls have been described as Neanderthaloid, but their resemblances to Neanderthal man are not close. Java has yielded, besides Pithecanthropus, a series of 11 skulls and two leg bones (tibiae) found at a place called Ngandong in a Late Pleistocene terrace of the Solo River 20 meters above the present water level. The first skull of Solo man, as he is called, was picked up by a native in 1931. The skulls are of small capacity and are widest low on the vault (see Fig. 11-3). They have marked supraorbital tori, but the foreheads slope away from these rather than being separated by a depression as in more typical Neanderthal skulls. The occipital torus is less marked, the cranial vaults are low, and the skulls are unusually thick. They are certainly not of modern type, but seem to be intermediate between Pithecanthropus and Neanderthal in many respects. In two cases the base of the skull is preserved. Unfortunately, this part is present in very few other specimens of fossil man, so that direct comparison is not possible; but Solo man resembles neither modern man nor Neanderthal man

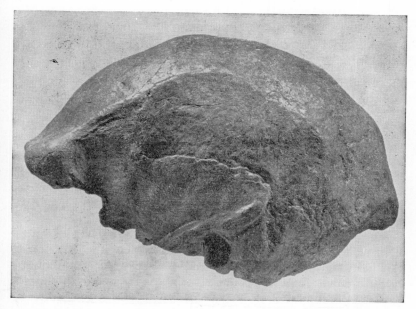

Fig. 11-3. One of the skulls of Solo man. It is low, and the supraorbital torus at the front (*left* in the photograph) is large but not separated from the forehead by a groove as in, for example, Neanderthal man. (Courtesy of the American Museum of Natural History.)

in this region of the skull. Weidenreich (1951) believed Solo man most similar to Peking man and would class Solo, Peking, and Java man together as Archanthropic, "Beginning Man," in contrast with Neanderthal and Neanderthaloids (Paleanthropic—"Old Man") and modern man (Neoanthropic). Weidenreich's monograph on Solo or Ngandong man was incomplete when he died in New York in 1948. It was published as he left it; the last sentence stops in the middle.

In Solo man the direction of the bone that holds the inner ear is angulated somewhat like that of the gorilla. The leg bones, like so many fossil limb bones we have discussed, are essentially like those of modern man. Although an overall statement is of dubious value, I would risk the comment that in skull configuration Solo man is more "primitive" than the European Neanderthalians and Neanderthaloids so far known.

The Discovery in the Quarry at Broken Hill, Rhodesia

The term Neanderthaloid has also been loosely extended to cover the human remains blasted from a quarry in Rhodesia, called Broken Hill, in 1921, by workmen mining the lead and zinc ores. Most of the specimens apparently pertain to a single individual. Rhodesian man, as he is called, is thought by some to represent roughly the same level of development as Solo man. The supra-orbital torus extends to the outer edges of the orbits and is larger than in any other known form of fossil man; in fact, it is comparable in size with that of the gorilla. The jaw also is enormous. The face is flat but protruding. The skull is flattened down, and the occiput has a torus. The area on the skull for attachment of the neck muscles is very similar to that of Solo man. All these characteristics have been mentioned before as "Neanderthaloid," but Rhodesian man also has distinctive features. The general shape of the skull is more like that of modern man, and the pelvis and limb bones are indistinguishable from those of men today. Incidentally, the robust jaw contained diseased teeth: Rhodesian man is the earliest fossil man known to have suffered from dental decay and dental abscesses; this bane of civilization also occurs occasionally in the australopithecines, however, and in living nonhuman primates. An upper jaw (maxilla) from another individual was found in the same place at Broken Hill and is apparently of the same antiquity. It is considerably smaller and is somewhat hollowed above the canine teeth, and in this respect is comparable with the big-boned types of modern man.

Other African Skulls Similar to that of Rhodesian Man

The second Rhodesian specimen has been largely ignored until recently. It can most readily be compared with a human skull from Florisbad in the Orange Free State in South Africa. T. A. Dreyer (1947), an African zoologist, found a skull there in a spring together with Middle Stone Age tools and fossils of extinct animals. The Florisbad specimen, however, is assigned by virtually all authorities to our own species, and probably would have received little attention were it not for the fact that no such type occurs in Africa today. A recent examination of carbon from the Florisbad deposit proves it to lack C^{14}; the technique used on this particular specimen, gives a minimum age of nearly 45,000 years. Such a date, if it applies to the skull, lends emphasis to the primitive "Neanderthaloid" features of both Florisbad man and, by inference, Rhodesian man— especially the massive brow ridges and rugged features of the latter. Nothing except dearth of geologically early human skeletons from Africa interferes with assigning Florisbad and the second Rhodesian specimen (hence plausibly also the first) to a single continuum.

A few years ago, at a place called Hopefield, near Saldanha Bay in South Africa, anatomists from the medical college of Cape Town, some 90 miles to the south, collected fossil bones from the surface where wind action had left them exposed. Together with such evidences of antiquity as fossils of an extinct kind of wild buffalo with enormous horns, they picked up a human skull cap and a fragment of mandible (see Fig. 11-4). The skull cap is almost exactly the shape of that of Rhodesian man. Insofar as it differs at all it is a bit smaller. The original Rhodesian skull thus seems to be one of a continuous array of African paleanthropic people of some antiquity, ranging from the Cape of Good Hope to Rhodesia or beyond.

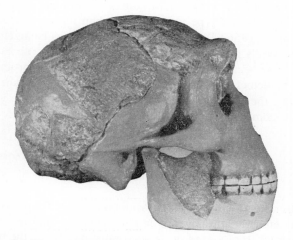

Fig. 11-4. Reconstruction of skull from Hopefield, Saldanha Bay, Africa. It is much like the skull of Rhodesian man and has a huge supraorbital torus. (Courtesy of the Wenner-Gren Foundation for Anthropological Research, and Ronald Singer.)

The Heidelberg Jaw

By now we have reviewed most of the known fossil forms that have significance for human evolution but are distinct enough from modern man to warrant placing them in separate species. In doing so we have omitted mention of several nonsapiens specimens that, because of uncertainties of affiliation, it is perhaps appropriate to take up separately. Best known of these is a jaw bone found by a workman in a sand pit at Mauer near Heidelberg. Since the discovery of this jaw in 1907, volumes have been written about Heidelberg man on the basis of this fragment. The stratum in which it lay has been dated to the latter part of the first interglacial period, or a period of temporary retreat of the ice during the succeeding glacial period—that is, some 450,000 years ago. If this date is correct, the find's seniority can be challenged only by the australopithecines, Pithecanthropus, and Peking man. The Heidelberg jaw itself is massive and lacks a chin. The teeth, however, are relatively small and are taurodont. This specimen is too robust to be Neanderthalian, but also fits in poorly with the Pithecanthropus and Australopithecus materials. It is similar to the Saldanha fragment. Perhaps the nearest thing to it is a mandible found in 1949 at Montmaurin, France, in association with stone tools of a type more ancient than those of Neanderthal man (Vallois, 1956). We may refer to this also as Neanderthaloid; if we had skulls to go with these jaws we could be more definite. Nevertheless, because of his primitive features and probable antiquity, Heidelberg man played an historically important role in establishing the broad outlines of human evolution in the years before more complete skeletons had been dug up elsewhere.

Several Big Jawbones from Africa

In Algeria, in 1954, Professor Arambourg (1955), paleontologist at the museum of natural history in Paris, pumped out the water from the deeper levels of a sand pit in what must have been the floor of a lake in Pleistocene times. Together with animal bones of species of the Early Middle Pleistocene he discovered two extraordinary mandibles. He also found flakes of stone and stone tools of a so-called "hand axe" or biface type in which chips are removed from both surfaces. This kind of industry occurs also in Europe, where it is called Chelleo-Acheulian and has been ascribed to Early Middle Pleistocene. The jaw bones themselves, one heavier than the other, conform in shape to those of Meganthropus but are not so large. The chin region is not developed at all. The teeth are taurodont and similar to those of Peking man. Despite similarities to these and also to Telanthropus, some anthropologists have assigned these jaws to a new genus, *Atlanthropus,* but it seems to me premature to segregate these fossils in a separate genus. Part of another mandible, collected in a gravel pit at Casablanca, Morocco, in 1954, has also been ascribed by Arambourg and Biberson (1956) to the same species. It is also reminiscent of Sinananthropus and is also associated with Acheulian tools. In this case, however, the tools are of a more developed type, and the site has been dated by a raised beach 100 feet above the present level of the sea. Arambourg believes that this beach was contemporary with the next to the last glacier. Whatever we call them, these jaws are of great importance because before their discovery we had no specimens with good claims of having belonged to the makers of Chelleo-Acheulian tools (save Swanscombe man; see below). These jaws are also important in providing a morphological link between the three Asiatic types—Sinanthropus, Meganthropus, and Pithecanthropus—and between these together and Telanthropus.

Still another possible link between Asiatic and African forms of fossil man comes from East Africa south of Lake Victoria. There, in 1939, Kohl-Larsen discovered a massive upper jaw that some identify with that of Meganthropus of Java and others equate with those of the australopithecines. We have no comparable parts of the Javanese Meganthropus, and it is safer to say only that this African specimen is from a massive-faced primate which, in our limited knowledge, is not significantly different from some australopithecines.

Dragon's Teeth

The last of the enigmatic fossils to be mentioned here are the least informative but most intriguing. In China the teeth of "dragons"

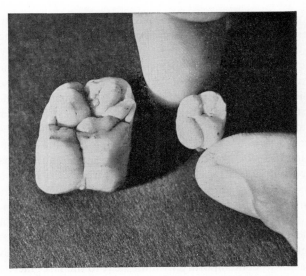

Fig. 11-5. Gigantopithecus upper molar compared with the corresponding tooth of present-day man. The similarity in pattern is as marked as the difference in size. (F. W. Goro, *Life*, copyright 1946, Time Inc.)

are believed to have curative properties, and, to meet the demand, enterprising pharmacists sell "dragon's teeth." These are fossil teeth of almost any kind. The vertebrate paleontologist G. H. R. von Koenigswald, who retrieved most of the known Pithecanthropus specimens, was aware of this custom and therefore made a practice of visiting the Chinese drugstores. On one such occasion in 1935 he was able to purchase three enormous molar teeth that have remarkably human cusp patterns (Fig. 11-5). These teeth are about three times the size of human teeth—quite outside the range of any living or fossil man, australopithecine, or even gorilla. What creature these so-called "Gigantopithecus" molars came from was quite unknown.

Without other parts of the skeleton, there could be no certainty as to what relevance these so-called "Gigantopithecus" teeth had for human evolution. From the color of the material that adhered to the teeth, and from other fossil bones of the same color, von Koenigswald inferred that they came from Early Middle Pleistocene cave deposits of Central China. Since the communist revolution in China, Dr. Pei Wen-chung (1957), one of the discoverers of Peking man, has encouraged the officials of that part of China to report any fossil bones to him and, as a consequence, in recent years has received 50 additional teeth. Once, a peasant called Chin Hsiu-huai, who was using cave bone to fertilize his fields, brought a fossil "dragon" bone to the marketing cooperative to try to sell it as medicine. The officials, realizing that it might be of scientific or cultural value, delivered it to Dr. Pei who identified it as a Gigantopithecus mandible. Subsequently two more such mandibles turned up in the same cave of Leng-Chai-Shan in Kwangsi Province where Chin had found the first one.

On the basis of the new evidence, Pei believes that Gigantopithecus was contemporaneous with Peking man. Pei also endorses the idea, first advanced by von Koenigswald, that Gigantopithecus is a giant ape rather than an apelike fossil man. No stone tools were found at the site, but it is strange that jaws from a nonhominid primate should come from a cave deposit. From the evidence Pei presents, it would appear that the jaw has some manlike features reminiscent of the big-jawed australopithecines, but that the front teeth of Gigantopithecus are larger. In the photograph, the first premolars also look more apelike than human. There is no reason to believe that the animals which possessed the teeth and jaws were gigantic. We should need other parts of the skeleton to draw such an inference. Garn and Lewis (1958) have shown that there is virtually no relationship between tooth size and body size either in modern man or in fossil forms; big-toothed forms are frequently short in stature. We must wait for more evidence before we can assign Gigantopithecus to its proper place in primate evolution.

GENERAL REFERENCE

Boule, Marcellin and H. V. Vallois, 1957, *Fossil Men*. New York: Holt, Rinehart and Winston, Inc. A general discussion of human origins by two authors who are especially familiar with various specimens of Neanderthal man.

12 · The Question of the Origin of Modern Types of Man

Swanscombe Man

As previously mentioned, the interpretation of any paleanthropic fossil rests on whether it antedates all neanthropic forms and could be ancestral to them. If a paleanthropic fossil is antedated by neanthropic forms, it has no more direct relevance for human evolution than a gorilla, a gibbon, or a globe fish—all more or less distant cousins of ours. They have all evolved through as many phases as we since our last common ancestors roamed the ground, the trees, or the seas.

The idea that modern types of man (*Homo sapiens*) have been on earth for a long time now rests mainly on the remains of skulls from two sites: Swanscombe and Fontéchevade.

At Swanscombe, England, in 1935 and 1936, A. T. Marston (1937), an English dentist who is also an amateur archeologist, found several pieces of a skull deep in a stratified deposit of the 100-foot terrace of the Thames River. The circumstances of the find were investigated and confirmed by a committee of the Royal Anthropological Institute. The associated stone tools are of Middle Acheulian type (hand axes and flakes). The bones found with the human skull are of animals which lived during the long second interglacial period. Furthermore, fluorine analysis of the human bones indicates a degree of fossilization comparable to that of the Middle Pleistocene animal bones from the same 100-foot terrace. Here we

117

have well-attested evidences of an antiquity greater than that of any of the Neanderthalian or Neanderthaloid specimens known. Unfortunately, however, the Swanscombe specimen is only a small fragment of the skull vault, a piece of parietal, and a part of the occiput. As far as these go, little except unusual thickness would appear to distinguish the remains from the corresponding parts of modern man. But there is also little to warrant the designation "neanthropic" except the lack of an occipital torus or other evidences of strong musculature. The skull, however, belonged to a young adult, perhaps only 20 years old, and the occipital and parietal parts of the skull of a weak young Neanderthaloid may not have differed much from those of *Homo sapiens*. Furthermore, as an African anatomist, M. R. Drennan (1956), notes, in shape Swanscombe man corresponds remarkably with Rhodesian man. Recently, after a number of unsuccessful attempts, additional bits of the same skull have been found. These match the old bits like pieces of a jig-saw puzzle, representing the counterpart of the earlier bones—that is, coming from the other side of the same skull. Unfortunately, therefore, they add little to our knowledge, and their study cannot be expected to permit us more definitely to associate the Swanscombe skull and *Homo sapiens*.

Fontéchevade I and II

In 1947, at a place called Fontéchevade, France, Mlle. G. Henri-Martin excavated parts of two skulls from the deposit outside the mouth of a cave (Vallois, 1949). It is believed that the cave roof extended over this part at the time these men lived, because the layer was completely sealed off by an overlying layer of stalagmite from the former ceiling of the cave. Above the stalagmite were strata containing stone tools of Mousterian type (the culture of Neanderthal man) and later Paleolithic types. The stone flakes found at the level of the skulls are of a coarse type called "Tayacian" and ascribed to the Lower Paleolithic. The animal fossils are of forms associated with a warm to temperate climate, hence consistent with a date of the last interglacial period.

Fontéchevade I is a specimen consisting of a small piece of frontal bone from the forehead. The brow ridges are of feeble development, such as occur in European women today. Fontéchevade II is a larger piece of bone from the crown of another individual. It also has a part of the frontal present; this shows a dent that has been taken to be the frontal sinus. On the basis of the location of this dent it is argued that there was no protruding frontal torus. The occiput is lacking. The skull is thick, as in Swanscombe man. There is no reason to call these fragments paleanthropic rather than neanthropic, however. The reverse conclusion also lacks proof, and Drennan points out that the contour of Fontéchevade II is not very different from that of a young Neanderthal man. The one distinctive feature, it seems to me, is that the frontal region, especially of the first specimen, is apparently of modern type.

Allegedly Early Specimens of a Modern Type of Man

At this point we may also mention a thick human occipital bone from cave deposits at Quinzano, Italy. It fits in better with the Swanscombe specimen than with Neanderthal man, but is too small a fragment to reveal its possessor's specific affinities; and the geological antiquity of the specimen likewise is in doubt.

In 1925, before the Swanscombe, the Fontéchevade, and even the Quinzano specimens were known, Sir Arthur Keith argued for the view that *Homo sapiens* has been around this world a long time. His argument was based on other specimens, which he believed to be ancient. It is interesting that each of these in turn has been cast into limbo and there is reasonable doubt today concerning their claimed antiquity. Some have turned out to be from interments into ancient deposits, some we simply do not know enough about, and at least one was a deliberate fraud. The "discovery" of allegedly ancient skulls of modern type and the subsequent arising of legitimate doubts has occurred repeatedly in Europe, especially in England. Similar claims of great antiquity have also been made for modern-type skulls from America. Africa, and Australia, but in none of these cases have claims to a date prior to the latter part of the Last Glaciation been substantiated by adequate evidence. One by one the claims have been opened to serious question.

"Piltdown Man"

Most famous of these specimens is certainly the so-called "Piltdown man," a cleverly arranged fake that associated parts of a very thick human skull of unknown origin with a piece of the jaw of an orangutan. Although many anthropologists had for years questioned the significance of "Piltdown man" for human evolution, it was not until 1954, forty-odd years after the alleged discovery, that those who had access to the original specimen finally tried to test the possibility of deliberate fraud. They found that the specimens had been ground, broken, dyed, and buried by a counterfeiter. Our view of human evolution is greatly simplified by discovery of the true explanation of the peculiar combination of features. In this case the original clue that something was amiss came from chemical tests of the fluorine content of the bone. They showed significantly less fluorine, hence less fossilization, than in bones from the deposits in which it was claimed "Piltdown man" had been found. Once alerted, it was relatively easy for investigators to notice the mechanical grinding of the teeth, chemical staining of the bones, and other machinations of the forger. The only problem remaining unsolved in this case is why anyone desirous of renown among scientists should have gone to so much trouble to invite the disaster of complete disrepute.

The same fluorine method indicates a relatively recent date for another skeleton, that from Galley Hill, which formerly was believed to come from an undisturbed deposit in one of the high terraces of the Thames River. Galley Hill man, entirely of modern type, must now be relegated to an unknown but relatively recent date. From similar tests, the London skull (sometimes called Lloyds), those from Baker's Hole, Bury St. Edmunds, Barcombe Mills, and probably the Wallbrook frontal bone can be considered intrusive in the English Glacial-age deposits in which they were found; so can the Moulin Quignon mandible from France. Fraud certainly need not be implied; rather, it is possible that these specimens could have been subsequently buried by man or become embedded by natural means in gravels of the glacial epoch.

Kanjera and Kanam

Before leaving the question of early specimens of our species, *Homo sapiens,* we should mention two discoveries made in Kenya, East Africa, in 1932. In an erosion gully in Middle Pleistocene lake deposit at a place called Kanjera on Lake Victoria, L. S. B. Leakey found parts of four human skulls and a piece of femur together with Acheulian-type stone implements. Some anthropologists have questioned the association, as the fragments from three individuals and some of those of the fourth were found on the surface. There is no doubt about the nature of the skulls, however; they are obviously of modern type and are said to be Negroid.

At Kanam, another place on the shore of Lake Victoria, a man named Juma Gitau, who was working for Leakey, found a piece of the anterior part of a mandible in a deposit that Leakey judged to be associated with a rich fossil fauna belonging to the Early Pleistocene. This dating would make it contemporary with the australopithecines. Leakey ascribed the mandible to a new species of man; it was associated with crude stone tools of a type called Kafuan. Many other anthropologists have described the jaw as modern in form and doubt its great antiquity. A cancerous growth on the mandible makes it difficult to judge whether there was a chin. Fluorine tests have been of no help in assessing the contemporaneity of Kanam and Kanjera men with Pleistocene fossils, because even modern bones from these places have a high fluorine content. Those who have recently reviewed the evidence believe the Kanam jaw was intrusive from a deposit of later date but that it is not modern. What is most needed, therefore, is further new exploration for remains of the makers of the Kafuan and Acheulian stone tools of East Africa.

Upper Paleolithic Man in Europe

By the time the last of the great glaciations was melting its way northward across Europe, the extinction of the great woolly mammoth and rhinoceros of that continent was being accompanied by the increase of herding animals: wild cattle, horses, and reindeer. The Upper Paleolithic men who hunted them and painted them on cave walls are known from a considerable number of fossil skeletons. These last men of the Old Stone Age turn out to be men entirely of our own sort, *Homo sapiens;* in fact, they belong to the same subgroup as Europeans—to what is usually (and inappropriately) called the "Caucasian Race."

One of the first discovered, hence most discussed, evidences of this people is from Cro-Magnon in the Dordogne Region of France. There, in 1868, L. Lartet found in a rock cleft the remains of at least five individuals. For a description of the skulls Lartet called on Paul Broca, better known for his study of the human brain—especially the area for speech. Broca assigned the skulls to a new Cro-Magnon race. The best preserved skull, that of an old man, has the facial features of a European. His brow ridges were large but were of the divided modern type and within the size range of those of man today. To judge by the length of the bones of the old man of Cro-Magnon, he was relatively tall. His face was short, but the skull was long. If a man of this type were to attract attention on the street today it would be only because of his clothes or his manners.

Numerous similar specimens have been found with the characteristic bone and pressure-flaked stone tools of the Aurignacian Solutrean, and Magdalenian culture periods. A skull from an early subphase of the last of these, called proto-Magdalenian, is illustrated in Fig. 12-1. The men and women of the Upper Paleolithic periods of Europe were all *Homo sapiens*. Those most similar to the "old man" are usually grouped collectively under his name as "Cro-Magnon man." Those which diverge in some respects are often given special designations. Thus Combe-Capelle is a somewhat widerheaded subtype in France; near the Czechoslovakian towns of Predmost and Brünn, rather heavy-featured skulls have been found that are named after these localities.

The Question of Racial Differences in Upper Paleolithic Times

Two European Upper Paleolithic finds are of special interest because some anthropologists have believed them comparable with

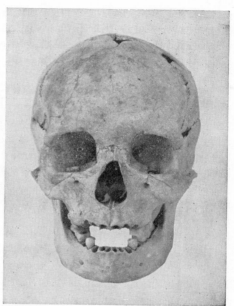

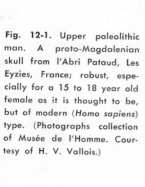

Fig. 12-1. Upper paleolithic man. A proto-Magdalenian skull from l'Abri Pataud, Les Eyzies, France; robust, especially for a 15 to 18 year old female as it is thought to be, but of modern (*Homo sapiens*) type. (Photographs collection of Musée de l'Homme. Courtesy of H. V. Vallois.)

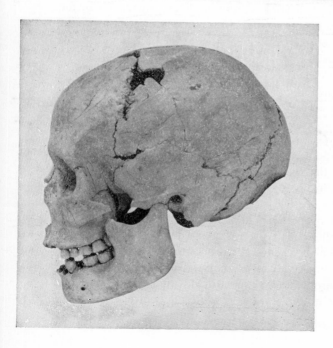

non-European modern races. In 1901, in a cave on the shores of the Mediterranean in the tiny principality of Monaco, L. de Villeneuve unearthed two burials in the Aurignacian layers. One is that of a child; the other, to judge from the skull, is that of an adult woman. These Grimaldi skeletons, so-called from the name of the ruling prince of Monaco, patron of the study, show some features resembling those of the Negro. The proportions of the limb bones, especially the relatively long forearm, are part of the resemblance. In addition, the skull is *prognathic:* The region of the upper jaw bone between the nose and the mouth tends to shelve slightly forward as in Negroes and some East Indians. On the other hand, other Negro skeletal features—especially the low, flat, wide nose—are lacking in the Grimaldi woman, and all traits are within the range now found among Europeans. I think that, insofar as one can tell from skeletons, the Grimaldi people were as much Caucasian as anything else.

The other skull of special interest is called Chancelade from the site in Dordogne, France, where it was found in 1888 by M. Hardy in a deposit of Magdalenian Age. The Magdalenian culture, last of the Paleolithic sequence, is characterized by bone tools: needles, harpoons, and fish hooks. Stone tools are small and include such types as engravers to etch decorations in bone. All artifacts greatly resemble the corresponding equipment of the Eskimo. Perhaps this fact influenced those anatomists who see Eskimo features in the Chancelade skull. It is certainly a narrow skull with a broad face and strong jaws, but this characterizes most Upper Paleolithic as well as Eskimo skulls. One special feature is a *palatine torus,* a longitudinal ridge along the roof of the mouth. It is true that a palatine torus is rarely seen in fossil man, but it is common in Lapps, Icelanders, and North Europeans as well as in Eskimos; if the reader will explore the roof of his mouth with his tongue, the chance is about one in five he will feel this characteristic, for at least a modest palatine torus occurs in about 20 per cent of adults in the United States. The Chancelade skull is not very different from that of other Upper Paleolithic men; there is no special reason to believe it related to the Eskimo. When a British anthropologist, G. M. Morant (1930–31), took the measurements of all the Upper Paleolithic skulls of Europe, including Grimaldi and Chancelade, he found that they are not very variable; quite the contrary, they conform to each other as closely as measurements of skulls from a single cemetery.

In general, the principal characteristics that differentiate continental populations today are not well reflected in the skeleton. Even if we could examine many Upper Paleolithic skulls from all parts of the world we might not know much about the origins of the races of the world. The record from outside Europe is sparse. Furthermore, the earlier skulls seem to have a certain uniformity: they tend to lack marked racial features and display instead a common set of characters such as ample jaw, narrow head, and large but divided brow ridges—that is, the hallmarks of Upper Paleolithic man in Europe.

If one thinks about it, it would be most surprising if the physical characteristics of a living race in any part of the world today could be exactly matched with a group of predecessors in the same region—or some other—ten thousand or more years ago. There is considerable evidence that large migrations took place in prehistoric as well as historic times. The newcomers, whether peaceful immigrants or conquering warriors, virtually always mingled with, rather than merely superseded, the indigenous people. Furthermore, as we shall note in more detail later, factors making for evolutionary change within racial groups have been present in relatively recent postglacial times and continue today; evolution is not something that happened once a long time ago and created then the races we see today.

The best-attested early skulls from Africa, for example, are not Negroid. In the case of the North African examples this is hardly surprising as, racially, modern North Africans fit in most closely with Europeans. But south of the Sahara, too, the earliest skulls are often described as resembling large versions of those of Bushmen or, in some cases, even of Australians. As already mentioned, the Florisbad skull is of modern type but somewhat reminiscent of Rhodesian man. I would not take this as evidence of long separate evolution in southern Africa, for I think that, superficially at least, the Florisbad man resembles the North African and even the East European *Homo sapiens* fossils.

In the Near East, too, as in North Africa, the Upper Paleolithic men as well as the modern inhabitants are physically similar to those of Europe. More or less typical Upper Paleolithic forms of skull have been found in Western Asia. The skeletons excavated by C. S. Coon of the University of Pennsylvania Museum from a cave at Hotu, Iran, and described by J. L. Angel (1951) are, except for the great height of the skull, not different from European specimens of the period in any important respect (see Fig. 12-2).

Three Skulls from the Upper Cave

In China at Choukoutien, the home caves of Peking man, there was an upper cave that was occupied at a later date. In it were three skulls together with Upper Paleolithic-type tools. Weidenreich (1939), when he examined the skulls, saw similarities between one of them and Eskimos, between another and Europeans, and between the third and Melanesians. The first is not specifically Eskimo; in fact it is hardly safe to call it Mongoloid, even in the widest sense, but it does have a wide, flat, midfacial region and a narrow skull. The second, thought to be the only male of the three and described as Protomongoloid by Weidenreich, is essentially Caucasoid in configuration—a big, rugged skull with short face and large brow ridges. Such a skull type occurs today not only in Europe but also among aboriginal Australians and among the Ainu of the northern islands of Japan. I would think of this as close to Upper Paleolithic man in general, but the proximity of China to Japan has suggested the Ainoid designation. The third skull is marked by a protrusive face, a feature of the Oceanic Melanesians; but one feature that may have influenced Weidenreich in his classifications is that the skull had been elongated during life, apparently by binding it round and round during infancy. This practice of skull deformation produces a similar head shape in some modern peoples, such as the Aymara Indians of Bolivia and Peru, and one or another form of head binding was formerly used by most American Indians to strap their babies to the cradle board.

Even if we must dismiss the literal implication of Weidenreich's handy designations, we are left with three well-attested Upper Paleolithic skulls in North China that show little in common with the modern Chinese. Although living contemporaneously (some suggest as husband and wives) in the confines of a small cave, they

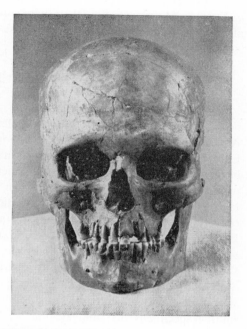

Fig. 12-2. One of the Upper Paleolithic skulls from Hotu, Iran; believed to be that of a female of about 35 years of age, not markedly different from Upper Paleolithic skulls of Europe (compare with Fig. 12-1). Although the cheek bones and jaws are strongly developed by modern standards, the skull is similar also to those of present-day Europeans. (The University of Pennsylvania Museum. Courtesy of Carlton S. Coon.)

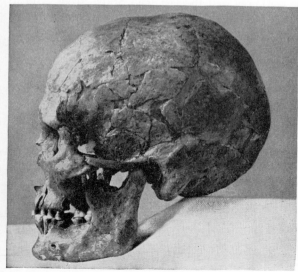

are about as diverse as the most extreme Upper Paleolithic types of Europe. At the same time they share some of the general features of the European Upper Paleolithic skulls.

Man in Australia and America

The same similarities to European Upper Paleolithic features may be seen in the most ancient human skulls from Australia and the Americas. In Australia present-day aboriginals also show some European Upper Paleolithic features. In the Americas there has been some question concerning the exact antiquity of Minnesota man from the United States, Tepexpan man from Mexico, and Punin man from Peru. As the carbon-dating method has reduced our previous estimate of the time span since the Last Glaciation in Europe, however, it has increased the established antiquity of the stone tools of the first human beings in the New World. Only a shallow channel, the Bering Strait, separates Alaska from Siberia. Since the sea was lower during glacial periods, America and Asia were repeatedly connected by land. From carbon dates of land and marine specimens that indicate the height of the seas at various times in the past, we know that the last land bridge from Asia to America existed from about 25,000 years ago until about 10,000 or 11,000 years ago (Hopkins, 1959). Man discovered America during that period if not earlier. Some of the known American skeletal remains may therefore pertain to the same period as the Upper Paleolithic in the Old World. The earliest definite date we have for a New World human skeleton is at least some 7000 years ago—a *Homo sapiens* skeleton of American Indian affinities, discovered at Midland, Texas, beneath a stratum containing an American type of Upper Paleolithic tool, the Folsom point (Wendorf and others, 1955). In general, the American skulls with the best claims to a considerable antiquity are somewhat but not markedly "Amerindian," as anthropologists sometimes call the American Indians. The early skulls also suggest the Australian or even the European with big brow ridges and prominent jaws. To me these are merely the common features of early *Homo sapiens* almost wherever he is found.

GENERAL REFERENCE

Howells, W. W., 1959, *Mankind in the Making.* Garden City, N.Y.: Doubleday and Company, Inc. This lively account of human evolution includes an exposition of Howells' views on the differentiation of the modern races of man.

GENERAL REFERENCE

13 · Human Genetics, the "How" of Man's Evolution

How Has Man Evolved?

We have reviewed some of the evidence for human evolution. We shall now raise the further question: "*How* has man evolved?"

To answer this will require division of the vast panorama of human prehistory into smaller units of a few generations, and the whole of humankind into little groups of people that can be studied closely. Evolutionary changes in man occur in the large, but we can learn more about them, their causes, nature, and rates, in the diverse small situations of the family and the tribe. There is much to be learned—by analogy—from experiments with the herds, flocks, and breeding colonies of domestic and protected animals.

In considering how man has evolved we shall want to limit ourselves to the inherent properties of men that are biologically transmitted from generation to generation. There is, of course, a "heredity" of acquired traits, through learnings of different sorts; but that is another story, though all too often it is confused with biological heredity by people who judge from their own observation that "Johnny walks just like his father" or "The Chinese are congenitally industrious." That story is the province of history and cultural anthropology. True, cultural and biological inheritance have certain interrelationships. Culture occurs only in beings who inherit certain essentially human biological capacities—notably, the mental capacity for symbolic thought and communication. And biological

131

inheritance is, as we shall see, affected by selection of mates and fate of offspring—events that are influenced by cultural factors. The further a group of humans evolves culturally, the larger this influence.

We shall here limit our discussion of cultural influences, however, to their effects on traits that are clearly part of the physical inheritance—more specifically, human genetics. In this field we must face, in particular, four questions: (1) In units of what kind can genetic transmission best be traced? (2) How may changes in the frequency of such units be traced from generation to generation? (3) What causes such changes? and (4) What circumstances, unconnected with genetics, may permanently affect the human body, and how may they be discerned so that we can allow for their influence when we try to identify and measure genetic units and their changes?

The Evolutionary Significance of Variability

Anyone who looks about him will see that people differ, even, to some degree, from their parents (see Fig. 1-1). They also differ at least slightly from their brothers and sisters. Some of these differences are in respect to hereditary characteristics. Although it is true that occasionally a pair of brothers or a pair of sisters are born essentially identical (one-egg, or *monozygous,* twins), this exception only calls attention to the variability of man in general.

Hereditary variability between people seems always to have been appreciable. Wherever several fossil skeletons are found in a single place and belonging to the same time they vary somewhat. For example, there is a considerable range of variation in the skulls, teeth, and jaws of the specimens of Peking man, Rhodesian man, Mt. Carmel man, and, as already noted, the "Upper Cave man" from Choukoutien, China.

Another evidence of the variability of man from "the beginning" is the fact that all other animals also vary. The primates are noteworthy in this respect. Professor Adolph Schultz (1937), a scholar who has reversed the usual trend and gone to Europe to teach after establishing a high reputation in the United States by his studies of primates, has repeatedly shown that the skeletons in the great apes vary in much the same way and to much the same extent as do human skeletons.

Darwin's theory of "natural selection" would require that a population undergoing evolution must vary. Selection would not be evolutionary if it took place merely among a number of identical beings. Darwin's theory rests on the premise of variation within the species in respect to characteristics that might to some extent fit or unfit the possessor for survival.

Mendel's Law: The Three-to-One Ratio in Genetics

Seven years after the appearance of Darwin's *Origin of Species* but five years before his *Descent of Man* was published, the proceedings of the natural science society of Brünn, in what is now Czechoslovakia, contained an article on a series of breeding experiments with peas carried on since 1856 in the small garden of an Augustinian monastery. The author, Gregor Johann Mendel (later abbot of the same monastery), had selected seven pairs of sharply contrasting characteristics for study. His next step was to cross peas contrasting in respect to each of these seven characteristics. In each of the seven instances the hybrids resulting from the cross were regularly of one or the other parental type, rather than intermediate between the two. Inheritance was clearly not a matter of blending. Furthermore, when the hybrid peas were self-pollinated (where the same plant serves both as "father" and "mother" and fertilizes its seed with its own pollen) Mendel noted that approximately three-fourths of the third generation showed the characteristic of the parent plant whereas one-fourth showed the characteristic present only in one plant of the original cross. Thus all crosses of round-seeded peas with wrinkled-seeded ones and vice versa resulted in rounded peas (Fig. 13-1); but when the hybrid round-seeded peas were planted and self-pollinated Mendel harvested almost exactly a 3 to 1 ratio (5474 rounded seeds and 1850 wrinkled ones).

To explain this ratio and its reappearance in the other six types of crosses, Mendel assumed that it was caused by formative elements (subsequently called genes). In the first hybrid generation

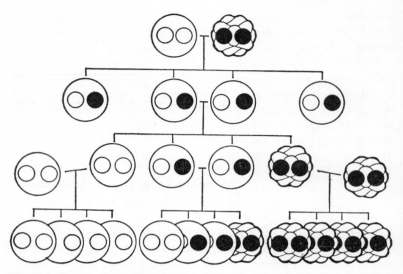

Fig. 13-1. Diagram illustrating Mendel's crossing of peas with smooth and wrinkled seeds (*top*), then self-pollinating the smooth-seeded hybrids (*second row*) to produce plants with smooth and wrinkled seeds (*third row*). The wrinkled and one third of the smooth ones breed true when self-pollinated (*bottom row*). Mendel's recessive and dominant formative elements (genes) are indicated by black and white dots. (From Ralph L. Beals and Harry Hoijer, *An Introduction to Anthropology*, Macmillan, 1953. Drawing by Virginia More Roediger.)

the formative element for wrinkled seeds was always paired with a formative element for rounded seeds. The formative element for the wrinkled character did not show up, however, when paired with a formative element for rounded. Mendel therefore called the element that showed up "dominant" and the one that did not "recessive."

The 3 to 1 ratio is just about what one would expect in such a case: In tossing two coins they will turn up one head and one tail in about half the tries, two heads in about one-fourth the tries, and both tails in one-fourth or so of the tries. If the tails were the "recessive" determiners there would be only about one in four double "recessive" tries: namely, two tails. Since in recessives the pair of determiners are of the same kind (like-paired, or *homozygous*), and there are no formative elements of the other kind, recessives will always breed true.

Mendel continued his plantings through successive years. His original varieties yielded consistent results when self-fertilized; so did homozygous recessive seeds. When the descendants of hybrids with the dominant characteristic—that is, with smooth rounded seeds—were self-pollinated, some bred true and some did not. The former may be presumed to have only one kind of formative element and are therefore also called homozygous for the characteristic in question. The third-generation plants that did not breed true must have had two different kinds of formative elements and are therefore called *heterozygous* (different-paired); like the original heterozygous hybrids, they gave about the 3 to 1 ratio.

As in the case of the two coins there are really three possibilities: two tails, homozygous recessive; two heads, homozygous dominant; and one head and one tail, heterozygous and showing the dominant trait. In all the cases Mendel studied, the heterozygous and the homozygous dominant were indistinguishable to the human eye. They could only be distinguished by further test plantings of self-pollinated seeds. Geneticists have coined the term *phenotype* to designate the visible characteristics and the term *genotype* to designate the inferred genetic constitution. In the case cited, the dominant phenotype, the rounded seeds, could occur in either of two genotypes—homozygous dominant, and heterozygous.

Independent Inheritance

Mendel also produced dihybrids by crossing peas in respect to two characteristics simultaneously, such as wrinkled peas in a smooth pod with rounded seeds in a constricted pod. The visible phenotype with both recessive characteristics occurred in about $\frac{1}{4}$ of $\frac{1}{4}$—that is, $\frac{1}{16}$ of the third generation—while the phenotype with both dominant traits occurred in some $\frac{3}{4}$ of $\frac{3}{4}$, or $\frac{9}{16}$. The remaining cases showed one dominant and one recessive trait. These experiments demonstrated that the genes acted independently of each other—rather like playing the black and the odd, against the red and the even, at roulette: A series of rolls that win on the black may win or lose on the odd.

The key observation from which Mendel formulated his theory was that when hybrids were bred with hybrids they produced certain types and proportions of constant progeny which henceforth bred true.

Human Chromosomes

As already noted in Chapter 3, genes are linked in chromosomes, and the chromosomes may be thought of as long strings of genes. Ordinarily the darkly staining material, chromatin, that constitutes the chromosomes is seen as a stringy mass in the nucleus that forms the functional center of most cells. When a cell divides and doubles during mitosis, the chromatin first sorts itself out into a discrete number of chromosomes. The moment just before division is called *metaphase,* and cells killed and suitably stained at this stage can be seen in the microscope to contain pairs of chromosomes in which the members of each pair are in close proximity to each other.

It was long believed that in man there are always 48 chromosomes in cells of body tissues. Recently the question of the number of human chromosomes has been restudied. This restudy has been facilitated by a new technique, *tissue culture,* by means of which cells of human and other tissues can be induced to grow and reproduce in a suitable medium outside the body. The cells can be squashed and spread out to photograph through a microscope, and the images of the chromosomes in the photograph can then be cut apart and mounted for counting and study. New counts of human chromosomes in tissue culture, and other recent counts, usually reveal 46 per cell with rare examples of 45 or 47 chromosomes per cell. The 46 chromosomes usually present consist of 23 pairs. The two chromosomes of a pair are not identical, however, for they differ in the genes for every characteristic for which the individual is heterozygous.

Sex-differentiating Chromosomes

Twenty-two of the 23 pairs of chromosomes are always matched in length and shape, and are called *autosomes.* In the human male, and in most other animals, however, one pair consists of one long and one short chromosome. The longer chromosome of the pair

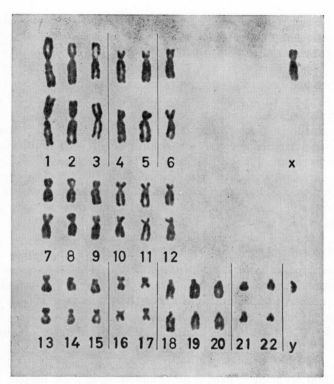

Fig. 13-2. Microphotographs of the 22 pairs and X and Y chromosomes of a normal male cell cut apart and remounted matched for form and size. In the normal female the Y chromosome would be lacking and there would be two X chromosomes. (From J. H. Tjio and T. T. Puck, "Somatic Chromosomes of Man," Proceedings of the National Academy of Sciences, 44, 1958. Courtesy of T. T. Puck and the Academy.)

is designated X and the shorter one, Y. Both are called *sex-differentiating* chromosomes. The male has one X and one Y chromosome (Fig. 13-2); the female has two X chromosomes and hence has 23 matched pairs.

The germ cells involved in reproduction, the *spermatozoa* of the male and the *ova* of the female, develop in a special manner called *meiosis*. As they mature they divide twice, and in one of these divisions they do not duplicate their chromosomes. In this way, the germ cell (*gamete*) gets only one of each pair of chromosomes: In genetic terminology, the *haploid* number in man is 23. In the reproductive process the mature spermatozoon and the mature ovum again fuse to produce a cell with a full complement of chromosomes, with the *diploid* number, 46. The offspring thus receives one of each pair of chromosomes from the father and one from the mother.

Since women have two X chromosomes, a child must receive an X chromosome from its mother, and its sex is therefore determined by whether it receives an X or a Y chromosome from its father. The offspring who inherit the father's X chromosome will have two X chromosomes and be female. Those who inherit his abbreviated Y chromosome will have an unmatched XY pair and be males.

Variations in Number of Chromosomes

Exceptions to the 46 chromosome count occur in hermaphrodites, individuals who are somehow intermediate between males and females in respect to formation of the reproductive organs. In one type of abberant "female" there are only 45 chromosomes (22 autosomal pairs and one X chromosome). In another condition, where maleness predominates, there are 47 chromosomes, two X's and a Y being present. In still another type of anomaly in which the individual is chiefly female, three X chromosomes are present. All in all it is the presence or absence of a Y, rather than the number of X chromosomes, that is most important in determining human sex. One anomaly of an autosomal chromosome is now well known. In the congenital disease named—or rather misnamed—mongolism (a disease involving mental defect) one of the autosomes is triple rather than double, and there are 47 chromosomes in all. A few other chromosomal abnormalities are known from rare sporadic examples. Conditions involving variation in chromosome number are hereditary in one sense, of course, but since the variation interferes with the capacity to reproduce, most such individuals are sterile, and the conditions do not seem to run in families. Incidentally, since the human chromosome number, 46, is not found in monkeys and apes, and since other details of man's chromosomal constitution are also apparently unique, it seems very probable that mating between men and apes would produce no offspring.

Linkage

In inheritance, the chromosomes tend to be transmitted as units. Each child receives only one of each pair from each parent. Since it seems accidental which one of each pair will be transmitted, inheritance of two traits on different chromosomes is completely independent. Thus in Mendel's peas the question of whether a pea was wrinkled or rounded, for example, was independent of whether the pod was smooth or constricted.

It is not always true that characteristics are inherited independently. Genes on the same chromosome tend to be transmitted together. They are said to be *linked*. Convincing evidence of linkage in man is exceedingly rare except for genes on the X chromosome. Linkage on the X chromosome is called sex-linkage, but the conditions so inherited have nothing to do with sex; they include certain types of color blindness and the bleeding disease, hemophilia. The gene for the usual form of the latter is rare. As it acts as a recessive in females, there is only a most remote chance of a female inheriting the gene on both X chromosomes and manifesting the disease. But if a female inherits it on one X chromosome, half of her sons will have the gene and in them there will be no paired chromosome carrying the normal gene; half the sons will therefore have the disease. In this way hemophilia has spread in several royal families of Europe, carried by normal females but manifest as a disease in some of their sons, including crown princes of Russia and Spain. A gene on the unpaired part of the X chromosome in a male is called *hemizygous,* half a pair.

Theoretically there should be a corresponding kind of linkage of genes on the unpaired part of the Y chromosome transmitted directly from fathers to all of their sons and none of their daughters; however, for man, no reliable reports of conditions of this kind are known, and there is probably no unpaired part of the Y chromosome.

One reason why linkage between genes on the same autosome has been so hard to discover in man is that we cannot experiment but are limited to observations of families that come to our attention. The genetic interpretation of such observation is not always easy, for what we observe is the outward characteristic, the phenotype. Indistinguishable phenotypes may represent several different genotypes, as we have noted in respect to Mendel's study of peas. Or, the same phenotype may sometimes result from environment rather than specific genetic causes; the propensity to bleed freely, for example, may be caused by vitamin K deficiency rather than hemophilia. Furthermore, the genotype, the genetic constitution that may be biologically transmitted to subsequent generations, may vary in its degree of prominence in the phenotype; in a hereditary disease, for example, the severity usually varies from patient to patient. Such individual variability in degree is called *expressivity*. In some cases a genetic characteristic may not be at all apparent in some proportion of individuals with the appropriate genotype; this statistical concept is called *penetrance*. A genetic characteristic with low penetrance is one that frequently fails to show up in persons who have the appropriate genotype. A dominant trait like abnormally short fingers frequently skips a generation, for instance, and is presumed to be present genotypically but not phenotypically in the skipped individuals. High penetrance means that phenotype and genotype correspond in a high proportion of cases.

Lack of complete penetrance and doubts about exact ascertainment of the genotype make it difficult to study genetic linkage in man. In order to establish linkage in human autosomes we need large enough studies to permit reliable statistical inference. These studies will need to include more or larger families than has so far been practicable.

Crossing Over

Another and more fundamental reason why only a large number of instances can yield conclusive evidence of linkage is that the pattern of linkage has a good chance of being reversed in any single instance. Chromosomes may break, in which case the parts may be transmitted independently. The most common form of this is *crossing over,* where, just prior to cell division, the corresponding parts of a pair of chromosomes are exchanged (Fig. 13-3). Places where a pair of chromosomes come in contact at this time are called *chiasmata* (crosses). Chiasmata can be seen in the microscope and are relatively common in man, averaging one or two per chromosome pair. Since the genes are arranged in a linear series on the

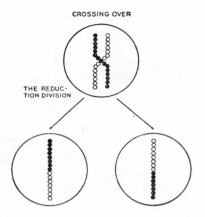

Fig. 13-3. Diagram showing how a pair of chromosomes (one made up of black dots, the other of white dots, *top*) may cross over so that at reduction division some linked genes (represented by the dots of like color) may become dissociated from each other and be transmitted in new combinations (*bottom*). (From Edgar Altenburg, *Genetics*, rev. ed., Holt, Rinehart and Winston, 1957.)

THE REDUC-
TION DIVISION

chromosome, the chance of a chiasma occurring between two genes is roughly proportional to the distance between the genes. Put the other way around, the frequency of crossing over of two linked genes is a measure of their distance apart on the chromosome.

Although there are numerous and excellent examples of linkage in autosomal chromosomes of corn, fruit flies, and mice, for man we are obliged to take a more or less hypothetical case, still inadequately verified, as an example. Let us suppose that a gene which to some extent determines body build occurs on the same chromosome as a gene disposing to freckles—that is, genes for body build and freckles are linked. Although some families would have more cases than expected of thin freckled and of stocky unfreckled individuals, there would be a deficiency of families of four types: (1) those with both freckled and unfreckled thin individuals; (2) those with both freckled and unfreckled stocky individuals; (3) those with freckled thin and stocky individuals; and (4) those with unfreckled thin and stocky individuals. Occasionally during transmission, however, the chromosomes would come together, form a chiasma, and break; and the genes could then recombine. In the case of genes for freckling and body build, this process would account for occasional families of the four types listed above, the cross-over types.

Crossing over assures that, for all but the most closely linked genes, inheritance over a number of generations of specific individual traits will be essentially independent. One cannot expect two linked hereditary traits to "go together" in groups of unrelated or distantly related individuals, although these traits will tend to go together within the family. That there are so many red-haired persons with freckles, for instance, is not because of linkage but is probably a multiple effect of a single genetic cause.

The frequency of crossing over assures that even linked genes are not a serious exception to the general rule of independent transmission of genes. Indeed, except for some characteristics whose genes are carried on the sex-determining X chromosome, such as color blindness, it has not been possible to assemble much satisfactory evidence of linkage in man. Our knowledge of linkage depends on experimental studies, not on statistical analyses of human families. For almost all the numerous hereditary traits we know in man, the inheritance of a gene or its alternate at the same locus on the chromosome (*allele*) seems a chance matter, in that our present state of knowledge does not permit us to predict which allele will be transmitted. Furthermore, the determination is essentially unrelated to the inheritance of other genes.

Mutual Adjustment of Characteristics to Each Other and to the Environment

In any organism the genes do not act directly as determiners of characteristics but rather as factors influencing growth or development of characteristics. However independent the genes determining them, the parts of an organism must fit together in some interdependent way. It is this secondary mutual readjustment of developing structures under the influence of new and frequently unique combinations of genes that makes it difficult to study the genetics of normally varying characteristics. Our knowledge of pedigree genetics is therefore fullest for sharply contrasting characteristics relatively unrelated to each other in terms of functional significance. In man we know more about the dominance and recessiveness of rare inherited diseases than about the mode of inheritance of body size or nose shape, for example. From analogy with studies of other animals and from surveys of man it seems safe to assume, however, that, although also influenced by environmental factors, many normal variations as well as numerous hereditary diseases are determined in part by single genes or the interaction of a number of independent genes.

Fluctuations in the environment from generation to generation can lead to a modification in the characteristics of the individuals who grow up in the environment. A return to the original environment would, however, probably lead to a return to the original characteristics in the offspring. Such changes based on the life experience of the individual are not known to have any permanent genetic effect except, in some instances, to permit survival of the group while genetic adaptations to the changed environment were evolving. All of the many experiments designed to test the inheritability of acquired characteristics have failed to establish a single valid case of its occurrence. Biologists therefore usually confine their concept of evolution to genetic changes and consider environmental factors only insofar as, through natural selection, they influence the establishment of different genes or different proportions of genes in the group under study.

Darwin and Mendel's Principles

Darwin seems never to have read Mendel's article, although there were copies in England and Darwin apparently consulted a book by Hermann Hoffman that referred to Mendel's work. Darwin's failure to read Mendel's paper or, if he read it, his failure to grasp its significance is surprising. Charles Darwin served as a sort of clearing house of biological information, and correspondents all over the world sent him publications and discussed new findings with him. Furthermore, Darwin himself had briefly toyed with the idea of particulate inheritance. Nevertheless, the idea and hence its application to evolution was to remain dormant until after the rediscovery of Mendel's work in 1901.

GENERAL REFERENCES

Colin, E. C., 1956, *Elements of Genetics,* 3d ed. New York: McGraw-Hill Book Company, Inc. An elementary textbook of genetics that presents Mendel's laws of heredity especially as they apply to man. The first six chapters, which deal with Mendelian principles, are especially recommended.

Stern, C., 1950, *Principles of Human Genetics*. San Francisco: W. H. Freeman and Company. Pages 542–604 on "Genetic Aspects of Race"; "Aspects of Race Mixture," and "Origin of Human Diversity" include a treatment of the social problems raised by a knowledge of genetics.

14 · Blood Groups

The application of human genetics to the question of human evolution could not proceed far merely on a knowledge of rare hereditary anomalies and diseases. The need was for a list of conditions that are inherited in a large proportion of normal individuals and whose relative frequency could be studied in various human populations. In recent years this need increasingly has been met by the growing list of blood group substances (Race and Sanger, 1954; Mourant, 1954).

Antibodies and Antigens

The biological behavior of blood group substances is essentially the same as that of bacteria: When the former are introduced into blood, they modify the protein in the serum so that it will react with additional amounts of the blood group, just as bacteria stimulate the production of antibacterial substances. These modified serum proteins are called *antibodies*. The study of these interactions is called *immunology* because, in the case of bacteria, the interaction of the antibodies with the bacterial substances actually destroys the bacteria and thus affords immunity to disease.

On the surface of the red blood cells are a number of substances, called *antigens,* that, when introduced into another individual, may form antibodies in his blood serum in the same way as is done by bacteria. Antibodies are capable of reacting with the specific antigen to which they correspond. The study of such reactions in man has permitted the classification of human antigens. The hereditary antigens are present from birth, and the individual keeps the same

145

kind throughout life. Possession of a particular antigen is inherited according to Mendel's principles.

Quite a number of different systems of antigens have been classified. Most of these are known to be inherited independently of each other; that is, there is no evidence of linkage in most cases. Different blood group antigens are therefore independent in evolution: Gene frequencies in one system can change while those in another do not. There are enough mutually independent systems of blood group antigens to permit anthropologists to use blood groups to relate groups of people today into historically meaningful patterns. When national or tribal groups are classed according to the frequencies with which they possess the genes for the different antigens, fewer and smaller differences are found to exist between neighboring groups and those with common origins than between groups of more distant origins. In other words, the blood group antigens provide an index of the genetic similarity of populations.

The ABO Blood Groups

The interest in blood groups sprang from the practice of blood transfusion—from animal to man or from man to man—which began at least as early as the seventeenth century. Although such experiments were frequently uneventful, in a few instances the recipient of the blood died following the transfusion. In 1900 Karl Landsteiner, who later received the Nobel prize for this work, discovered why. He noticed that when the red cells from the blood of one individual are mixed with the serum of another, the cells may clump—a reaction called agglutination. Landsteiner (1945) and his students found that they could group human beings into four types on the basis of these reactions, and that the four types could be explained by the presence or absence of either or both of two substances (antigens) in the cells. The property of agglutination was soon associated with the transfusion accidents, and blood typing for purposes of blood transfusion began.

The two antigens can be identified by tests using two types of antisera. These are called anti-A and anti-B. When a drop of anti-A serum is added to a drop of blood, the red cells may remain in normal suspension or they may react by clumping together. This reaction can be seen under a microscope or even with the naked eye. If the blood reacts to anti-A it must contain the A antigen. If the blood reacts to anti-A but not to anti-B, it is therefore called type A; if, conversely, it reacts to anti-B but not to anti-A, it is type B; if it reacts to both anti-A and anti-B, it is called type AB; and if it reacts to neither, it is called type O.

Although it was believed from the start that the blood groups were inherited, it took 25 years before enough evidence had accumulated to permit a German mathematician, Felix Bernstein (1924), to describe the mechanism. He showed that the inheritance of the blood groups could be explained as due to three alleles. The gene for antigen A (designated I^A) and for antigen B (designated I^B) are equally dominant, but that for O (designated i) is recessive; thus, as each individual could have only two of the genes (one on each chromosome), all human beings would be $I^A I^A$, $I^A i$, $I^B I^B$, $I^B i$, $I^A I^B$, or ii. But $I^A I^A$ would be indistinguishable from $I^A i$, and $I^B I^B$ from $I^B i$. In all authenticated cases of parents and children tested, the types found would be possible according to this system. Thus, for example, two type AB ($I^A I^B$) parents can never have a type O (ii) child, and two type O (ii) parents can have only type O offspring. This principle can be used to demonstrate that a particular man is not the father of some putative child; that is, in a particular case we can test the blood of a child and that of its mother and say that the father must have been of one or several types and could not have been of any other type. Such evidence has been used in court cases of disputed fatherhood, although some courts have not accepted the evidence. In some instances identification of the blood type of the red cells of a bloodstain has permitted police officers to say that the blood is not that of some particular suspect or victim. Furthermore, antigens similar to those of the human blood groups react with blood of different species and permit experts to determine whether a certain bloodstain is human at all.

The reason that transfusions of blood of the wrong type (or from any other species of animal) produce serious and sometimes fatal results, is that human blood contains antibodies as well as antigens. Fortunately, blood donors of type O have red cells that are not normally clumped and destroyed by anyone else's serum, and so group O persons are called universal donors: In an emergency, their blood can be given to anyone.

MNS and P Substances in Human Blood

Karl Landsteiner, the discoverer of the blood groups, continued his experiments, and in 1927 he and one of his associates discovered that, after injection of rabbits with human blood, a few of the animals produced an antiserum capable of reacting with some, but not all, human blood specimens (Landsteiner and Levine, 1927). The substance thus identified was designated M. It differs from the A and B substances in that the antibody was not found in human blood; to test for the human antigen the antibody was prepared in rabbits. A second substance, N, which occurs in some individuals who have M and in all non-M individuals, was soon found by Landsteiner and Levine. It is now generally believed that there are two genes, *M* and *N*, which correspond to the two substances. The two genes are alleles; that is, they occupy the same relative position on each of a pair of chromosomes. The individual with an *M* gene on each of a pair of chromosomes is of type M; likewise the individual homozygous for *N* is of type N; but the blood of heterozygous individuals reacts with both kinds of antisera, and they are of type MN. There is thus no Mendelian dominance. *M* and *N* are expressed equally.

More recently two new antisera, anti-S and anti-s, have been reported. One or the other of these reacts with all blood specimens. S and s are closely related to M and N because the frequency of S is not the same in individuals of type M, MN, and N. The exact genetic relationship of S and s to M and N is not quite certain, however.

Landsteiner and Levine also discovered a third type of antiserum in rabbits, one which identified a human antigen they called P. This is independent of the ABO and MNS system. In the past, however, the test sera for P have often been unreliable, and little anthropological use has been made of this reaction.

The Rh Factor

Beginning in 1939, Landsteiner and his associates—especially Philip Levine and A. S. Wiener—made another series of discoveries. In that year Levine and R. E. Stetson noted an unusual case of a woman patient of blood group O whose serum agglutinated blood of her group O husband during a transfusion. When tested it also agglutinated the blood of some other group O persons. The following year Landsteiner and Wiener (1940) injected rabbits with the blood of rhesus monkeys and found that the resulting antibodies in the monkey blood serum agglutinated not only the blood of other monkeys but also that of some people. The serum from the injected monkeys and that of the patient studied by Levine and Stetson reacted with the same blood specimens and therefore contained the same antibody. It has been called anti-Rh because it reacted with the blood of rhesus monkeys.

In the years since the original discovery, a series of subtypes of the Rh antigen have been established. According to one view these are caused by the presence of various combinations of dominant genes (C, D, and E) or their recessive alleles (c, d, and e) on a small segment of the chromosome responsible for the Rh type. If this theory of linked genes is correct, the linkage must be very close, because authentic cases of crossing over are hard to find. The alternative view is that enough different kinds of allelic genes appear at the one locus to account for the variety of Rh types. This sharp difference of opinion may be in part nothing more than a difference in views concerning the nature of the gene. The gene is, after all, an abstract concept describing the genetic behavior of what is probably a segment of chromosome with a particular sequence of base bars of DNA. The exact limits of such a segment cannot be determined. Whether a variation is considered to lie within a gene (allelic difference) or in closely linked genes along the chomosome will depend on the arbitrary boundaries assigned to the gene.

Additional Blood Types and the Secretor Factor

Not only are there subgroups of Rh, but there are also several known subtypes of A, M, and N. In addition there are a large number of other antigens that are independent of the previously mentioned systems or related in still unknown ways. These are usually named for the individual in whom the antigen was first found and bear surnames such as Lutheran, Lewis, Kell, Duffy, Kidd, and Diego.

One additional factor related to the blood groups is of at least potential value in anthropology. In some individuals of groups A, B, and AB the blood group substances are found in saliva and in other body fluids; in other persons of the same groups the substances are not dissolvable in water and do not occur in the saliva. Furthermore, there are a number of anti-O and so-called anti-H antibodies, derived from various animals and plants as well as from human blood, that permit testing of group O individuals to see whether they possess O-antigen in soluble form. Most secretors also have the Lewis antigen, but it is doubtful that these are two results of a single gene. One possible linkage is that of the Lewis gene with the one for the Lutheran blood group.

Persons lacking A and B antigens always have the corresponding antibodies. In the other blood group systems antibodies are not normally found in individuals who lack the antigen. These other systems therefore have less practical significance for blood transfusion. Nevertheless, from the point of view of genetic research, these factors are equally interesting. Taken in aggregate, the blood groups permit geneticists to plot the frequency distribution of a considerable number of human genes. At least one anthropologist, William C. Boyd (1950), one of the first and strongest advocates of the application of genetic methods to anthropology, has used the distribution of the blood group genes to divide mankind into races. Most other anthropologists would agree that the method is, at least, a valuable adjunct to other methods of racial classification.

An Example of Blood Group Anthropology: The Case of the Basques

As an example of the use of blood groups in racial anthropology we may cite the case of the Basques, inhabitants of the Western Pyrenees and a strip of coast on both sides of the frontier between France and Spain. The Basques have long attracted the interest of anthropologists because of their unusual language. Most European languages are related to each other, being of Indo-European stock; the languages of Finland, Estonia, and Hungary are members of another stock, Finno-Ugric. Basque is the only language of Europe that is unrelated to either group; in fact, it is not clearly related to any other known language. Furthermore, the Basques have retained a number of folk practices such as the *couvade,* wherein during the confinement of a woman her husband also takes to his bed.

Some anthropologists have concluded that the Basques are a remnant of an early widespread population who sought refuge in the mountains and thus survived the numerous historic invasions of southwestern Europe. The Basques have been thought to resemble Upper Paleolithic man. There are, however, only small differences in such traits as head form and eye color between Basques and other Europeans. But when the ABO blood groups were studied, it was noted that the Basques have an unusually low proportion of the gene I^B. This is true, but not quite so pronounced, in some other isolated or peripheral peoples: The Lapps of Scandinavia are low in I^B but high in I^A, and peoples of the Western Caucasus are low in both I^B and I^A and very high in i. The Basques, like the peoples of Europe in general, have a high frequency of blood group A; and, like other Europeans but unlike all other peoples of the world, there is a considerable proportion of group A individuals belonging to the subgroup A_2. The ratio of M to N in Basques is also in the European range. When it comes to the Rh frequency, however, the Basques reach a world maximum in the proportion of Rh-negative persons.

On the basis of the differences between Basques and other Europeans, Boyd has suggested that an earlier population group in Europe had a high incidence of Rh-negative and no blood group B. How long ago such a group was widespread we do not know, and it would be hard to determine because rates of change in gene frequencies are the result of several interacting factors, any one of which may be difficult to measure.

The Mixed Blood Fallacy

The lesson we have learned from Mendel's peas is simply this: Hereditary characteristics are transmitted as wholes, and descendants are not the result of mixing. In sexually reproducing plants (and animals) the offspring inherit whole genetic units (genes) from their parents, and these determine the characteristics of the offspring. The idea of "mixing of blood" is quite unsound. A mulatto does not inherit half his blood from the white and half from the Negro parent; he inherits a set of genes from each, and genes cannot mix. Except for those on the chromosomes that determine sex, in males, he gets an equal number from each parent. But he gets only half of each parent's supply, and there is no way of predicting which half. Such a child will probably be intermediate between his parents in characteristics determined by several genes, but he is unlikely to be just half way between in any of them. Although blood does not "mix," it does preserve blood group substances derived from ancestors. A wide variety of antigens that are inherited as unit characters in known ways stand ready to tell us something of the probable affiliations of populations.

GENERAL REFERENCE

Boyd, W. C., 1950, *Genetics and the Races of Man.* Boston: Little, Brown and Company. Chapters IV through IX (pages 108–276) contain an analysis of genetic factors in evolution and the use of blood groups in human classification.

15 · Population Genetics: Changes in Gene Frequencies from Mutations and Natural Selection

Evolution: Change of Gene Frequency in the Breeding Population

Darwin's main contribution to the understanding of evolution is the theory of natural selection. Of two somewhat different plants or animals, the one whose inherited characteristics better adapt it to life under a given set of prevailing circumstances has the better chance of leaving offspring. This is true whether or not the competing organisms belong to the same group, so long as they are living the same kind of life in the same place. Natural selection not only means "the survival of the survivors," it also implies that on the average a new generation composed of the offspring of such survivors will be more fit than the last generation. Since the new generation is descended from the fittest members of the last generation, evolution progressively favors the genetically fit. In the century since Charles Darwin and Alfred Wallace independently arrived at this principle, no data have been uncovered to contradict it, and much confirmatory evidence has been advanced.

In the last 30 years or more, however, Sewall Wright (see, for instance, 1932, 1938) and Theodosius Dobzhansky (1951), two American geneticists, and their British counterparts, R. A. Fisher

(1930) and Julian Huxley (1943), have applied genetics to the analysis of evolution. The studies of these investigators, among others, start by defining as "evolutionary" any event that alters the frequency with which specific genes occur in a subsequent generation. Any circumstance that causes a group to change systematically in gene frequencies generation after generation is, by definition, a significant factor in the evolution of the group. The development of particular combinations of genes may be the most significant form of evolution, but this is merely a special case, and the pattern is seen only after the event. Simultaneous changes in several gene frequencies must stem from the same basic causes as change in the frequency of a single gene.

The Breeding Population

The anthropologist Frederick P. Thieme (1952) has called attention to the problem of defining the group in human populations. He points out that, in man, religious, caste, racial, economic, educational, class, and other cultural factors affect the selection of mates, hence the social groups which the geneticist would call breeding isolates. Before we can study ongoing evolution in man, we must define such subgroups. The *breeding group* may be thought of as that social group within which mates are ordinarily found, the *endogamous* group of the social anthropologist. It is bound together by intermarriage and hence shares a "pool" of genes. The ways in which the gene frequencies of such a group may be altered can be listed as mutation, natural selection, random selection, and degree of isolation. Evolution may be defined as the change in gene frequency resulting from the interaction of all such factors.

The professor of physical anthropology at the University of Wisconsin, William S. Laughlin, has emphasized the importance of the study of local groups to an understanding of evolutionary processes in man. He writes that variation is encountered between contemporary members of a group and between contiguous groups (Laughlin, 1960). Furthermore, inferences can be drawn concerning variation within breeding groups with time, which is evolution.

Gene frequencies or the frequency of hereditary physical traits in a number of contiguous populations can be plotted on a map. In such a map most traits will have one or more centers of high frequency, and the frequencies will tend to fall off more or less rapidly

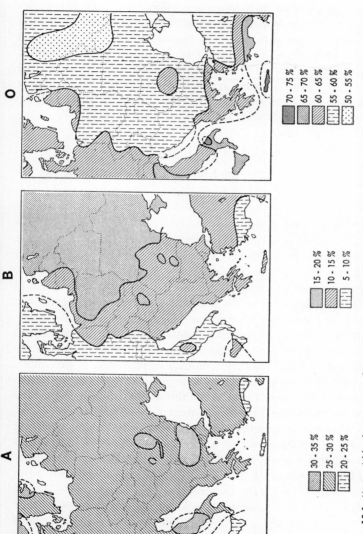

Fig. 15-1. Maps of blood group gene frequencies in eastern and central Europe. Areas with different frequency appear as slopes, or clines. The frequency of the gene for B (I^B) slopes down from east to west while that for O (i) shows a reverse trend. Along the shores and on the islands of the Mediterranean there are more local configurations. (From A. Manuila, *American Journal of Physical Anthropology*, 14 (585), 1956. Courtesy of the author and the Journal.)

A
30 - 35 %
25 - 30 %
20 - 25 %

B
15 - 20 %
10 - 15 %
5 - 10 %

O
70 - 75 %
65 - 70 %
60 - 65 %
55 - 60 %
50 - 55 %

to areas of low frequency. If lines are used to connect places where the particular trait has the same frequencies, the result is a "contour" map with "slopes," or *clines,* running up from centers of low frequency to those of high frequency (Fig. 15-1). The angle depends on the degree of intermixture between contiguous population isolates and the rate of evolution within the isolates. The clines will be steeper where there is relatively little *gene flow,* the term applied to the genetic result of intergroup mating. Professor Joseph Birdsell of the University of California at Los Angeles (1951), who is chiefly responsible for introducing these concepts in physical anthropology, has used such maps to shed light on the genetic prehistory of the Australian aborigines.

Stability of Gene Frequencies; Sex Ratio

Before discussing changes, we should first clear up one common fallacy: Dominant genes do not become more frequent at the expense of recessive ones. In the absence of other factors, gene frequencies in a population will remain the same from generation to generation. The term "dominant" merely means that when a dominant and a recessive allele occur in an individual, the dominant gene will determine the outward appearance (the phenotype). The likelihood of the recessive gene being transmitted is not diminished; in other words, a child has an equal chance of inheriting any of the genes of each parent—be they dominant or recessive. For example, two parents of blood group A both carrying the gene for A (I^A, the dominant) and the gene for O (i, the recessive) will transmit, on the average, as many i as I^A genes to their progeny.

This principle in genetics is called the Hardy-Weinberg law. It states that, if the frequency of a certain gene, A, is $p,$ and the frequency of another allele, B, at the same locus, is $q,$ then the distribution of the genotypes AA, AB, and BB in the population will be in the ratio of the terms in the expansion of $(p + q)^2 = p^2 + 2pq + q^2$. If B is taken to represent all alleles at the locus except A, then $p + q$ equals unity and $q = 1 - p$. It should be understood that if $p + q = 1$, then $(p + q)^2 = 1$. These facts can be used to estimate gene frequencies from known frequencies of the homozygous recessive. Thus in a randomly breeding population with 16 percent Rh-negative individuals, the quantity $^{16}/_{100}$ is equal to p^2 in the equation $p^2 + 2p(1 - p) + (1 - p)^2 = 1$, and the square root of $^{16}/_{100}$, which is $^4/_{10}$, is equal to p: This is the gene frequency of A. The remaining $^{84}/_{100}$ of the population which is Rh-positive is accounted for by the last two terms of the expression $2p(1 - p) + (1 - p)^2$, giving the relative proportions of heterozygous and homozygous Rh-positive individuals, respectively. Substitution of $^4/_{10}$ for p in these terms gives the numerical values for the two portions of the Rh-positive population: $2 \times {}^4/_{10} (1 - {}^4/_{10})$ and $(1 - {}^4/_{10})^2$ equals $^{48}/_{100}$ AB heterozygotes and $^{36}/_{100}$ BB homozygotes. The sum of these two is $^{84}/_{100}$. Notice that the $^{36}/_{100}$ of the population that is homozygous with respect to B may in fact be heterozygous, since B represents all alleles at the locus except A.

There is an apparent discrepancy in respect to sex: The sexes, themselves genetically determined, are not born in equal numbers. More males are born than females; in the United States, for example, approximately 105 boys are born for every 100 girls. Of course the discrepancy does not progress from generation to generation: Every child has just one father and one mother. There are fewer females than males, but more children are born to the statistically average female than are fathered by the average male. More males die young, marry late, or remain bachelors.

The unequal sex ratio does not seem to be due to differences in the prenatal death rates, for there are, if anything, more miscarriages of male fetuses. The inequality is thought to be in some way related to the differences in the chromosomes which determine sex, the X and Y chromosomes, but the supposed relation is not clear. One notion is that male-determining spermatozoa may be slightly lighter (since one chromosome, the Y, is small) and hence may move faster than female-determining ones.

Mating between Closely Related Individuals

Even with no change from generation to generation in the relative frequency of different genes in a population, there is one situation in which the proportion of genotypes may vary. This variation arises because, although the proportion of genes remains constant, the ratio of homozygous to heterozygous individuals may not. Related individuals—say cousins—are more likely to share the same kind of genes than are unrelated individuals. If related individuals mate (in so-called consanguineous marriage) there is, therefore, an increased chance for the offspring to receive the same kind of gene from both parents. Such a pair of genes is homozygous, like-paired. We have already noted that recessive traits are visible in the phenotype only when they are homozygous. Recessive phenotypes therefore occur more frequently in inbred populations. Consequently, consanguinity is more often found in the parents of persons known to have recessive traits. It was high frequency of cousin marriages in the parents of persons with three congenital anomalies (albinism, cystinuria, and alkaptonuria—respectively, depigmentation and the tendency to excrete one or the other of two special substances) that A. E. Garrod saw as evidence of Mendelian inheritance in man soon after the rediscovery of Mendel's work. We should add that the rarer the recessive condition, the less likely it is to occur except in the offspring of related persons. One seldom sees an albino, a person with ivory white hair and pink skin and eyes, for example, and a considerable fraction of the total number of cases are the children of cousin marriages. Taking all abnormalities into account, defective offspring are somewhat more common in the children of consanguineous than nonrelated matings. The rate of defective offspring of first cousins is less than double that of the general population.

In considering the desirability of marriages between cousins or other relatives, it is well to bear in mind that, although there is a somewhat higher chance of the offspring's having any rare recessive disease, inbreeding will not affect the likelihood of inheritance of dominant traits and will have a negligible effect on the expectancy of any conditions that are frequent in the general population. Furthermore, from the point of view of society, any increase in the number of deleterious homozygotes that may occur does not represent an increase in the number of genes with deleterious effects. One generation of outbreeding would offset any degree of inbreeding no matter for how long it has occurred.

Mutation — *sudden change in characteristic.*

The first of the four ways in which gene frequencies can change, in fact the only way in which totally new possibilities arise, is through spontaneous change in the genetic material—a change that can be transmitted. Several varieties of such changes have been observed in the chromosomes and genes of plants and animals, the most important from the evolutionary viewpoint apparently being a change that occurs in a single gene—that is, gene mutation. A gene mutation can be defined as a spontaneous change at a single locus on a chromosome (perhaps only one or a few base bars of DNA) rather than an alteration of a large segment or a whole chromosome.

It has been argued that mutations could have little to do with evolution because those actually observed in the laboratory or in man are nearly always detrimental (or at least neutral). It seems to me that this argument has little weight, for no one would claim that mutation alone produces evolution. It would do so chiefly in the presence of other factors, such as natural selection, and would merely account for the presence of variation. In a more or less well-adapted animal or plant, most changes would be for the worse, assuming environmental conditions to remain unchanged. But in a period of changing environment or new opportunities, an occasional mutation might well "take hold." So far no one has been able to predict which genes will mutate nor the direction mutations will take, although mutations can be greatly increased in frequency by some chemicals, such as mustard gas, and especially by x-ray and other types of radiation.

Mutations are generally disadvantageous—for the simple reason that the form or organ that changes is already the outcome of a chain of natural selection for fitness that reaches far into the past. Nevertheless, the capacity to mutate (but at a low rate) is itself selectively advantageous. With a changing environment a species may be able to tolerate disadvantageous mutations for the sake of an occasional advantageous one. Were it not for the possibility of change and its occurrence in one individual or a few individuals, the whole evolutionary line might be destined to extinction. This may explain why mutation is an attribute of all living things. The rates of mutation are normally between about 5 and 50 per million births. Some such rate may be the optimum, naturally established through selection.

Recently, alarm has been expressed concerning the genetic effects on man of experiments with radioactive weapons. Most mutations are harmful, as we have noted, and each increase in radioactivity tends to increase the rate of mutation in man. Therefore, as one geneticist, Nobel Prize winner Professor H. J. Muller of the University of Indiana, has put it, we are increasing "our load of mutations." If this increase is minor, natural selection (through death and sterility of *mutants,* the carriers of mutations) can probably maintain our species. There is, however, some disagreement among qualified experts as to what can safely be considered "minor." Actually, there is no set limit. There is no way accurately to predict the genetic effect on mankind of hydrogen bomb experiments, discharge of waste from atomic energy installations, or the widespread medical use of diagnostic x-ray. So far we have probably raised natural human mutation rates proportionately little, but we have no safe way of counting "moderate" increases in undesirable recessive mutations or of appraising their possible long-run effects. Any penetrating radiation that reaches the ovaries or testes is capable of producing inheritable mutations in germ cells. The number of such mutations is proportional to the length and intensity of exposure to such radiation. But, again, we have no way of predicting exactly which cells will mutate or what mutations will ensue. Toying with radiation is like playing Russian roulette: We know the gun is loaded, but we cannot tell in which chamber until the fatal shot is fired.

Natural Selection

Natural selection, the second factor in evolution, is clearly important in modifying whole species and higher taxonomic orders. In some situations, for example, faster species of antelope have had better chances to survive than slower types. The question of natural selection in relation to subspecific differences is another matter, however, and serious doubt remains concerning the evolutionary origin of the differences between human races. It is not easy to find examples of natural selection at work in modern races. We can only guess what advantages to survival in given circumstances there may be in blond human hair, or dark skin, for instance. One of the most dramatic cases of evolution within a subspecies (microevolution) is the change of color of many species of English moths. In recent years, with the increasing prevalence of smog, the moths have darkened appreciably. Color in these moths is an inherited characteristic, and the dark moths apparently have been selected for survival in the darker environment. Under modern industrial conditions they are less conspicuous to birds which would have preyed on them had they retained their former color.

The idea of natural selection is quite simple; its actual working out is more complex; and its predictive application to problems of survival, all but impossible. For example, wide areas of the world have received large numbers of European colonists, African slaves, and Chinese coolies, and these and other physical types have succeeded in establishing themselves in a wide variety of environments. Diversity within the population itself seems adaptive. All groups of man studied show considerable biological variability. Human populations have both larger and smaller, stronger and weaker, more aggressive and more complacent members. This variability probably is a reflection, in part, of genetic diversity. The advantages for the group of genetic diversity among its members probably accounts for the preservation of considerable variability in respect to numerous characteristics in man.

The term *balanced polymorphism* is used in population genetics to describe a situation in which the forces of natural selection maintain a diversity within a species. In balanced polymorphism an equilibrium exists in which several different alternative alleles are maintained in a population. If the heterozygous individuals Xx of a gene X and its allele x are more viable and are to some extent favored for survival both over individuals who are homozygous XX and those who are homozygous xx, the population is likely to achieve a balanced polymorphism. Both X and x genes will tend to be maintained in the population by the selection for survival of the Xx individuals. Since matings between two Xx individuals will produce roughly one XX and one xx individual for every two Xx individuals, selection will continue in every generation. Furthermore, depending on the relative pressure of selection against XX

and xx individuals, there will be some ratio of X to x in the general population that will be in equilibrium. That is, in balanced poly-morphism there is some ratio of X to x at which any increase in the relative frequency of either allele will tend also to increase the force of natural selection against that allele and thus tend to return the ratio to its former balance.

Sickle-cell Disease, an Example of Natural Selection

One well-known genetic condition seems to be an example of balanced polymorphism in which complex selective forces are at work. *Sickle-cell disease* is a serious anemia, usually fatal before adulthood. It occurs in persons homozygous for a certain gene that determines the nature of hemoglobin, a chemical constituent of red blood cells. This gene is relatively frequent in some tropical peoples of Africa and India, and in Negroes and their descendants in other parts of the world. The question arises as to why the severe natural selection against the gene for such a condition would not have kept the frequency of the gene to a very low level.

In this case we have tests that permit us to distinguish among three types: heterozygous individuals, "normal" homozygous ones, and the diseased homozygous ones. That is to say, there is no dominance. One of the tests consists of keeping a drop of the blood away from the oxygen of air. After a period of time the red blood cells of a homozygous anemic person assume bizarre sickle-like shapes when viewed under a microscope (Fig. 15-2). The red cells of the heterozygous individual also "sickle" but much more slowly and in less extreme shapes. The red cells of the homozygous "nor-mal" do not sickle at all.

A more refined test, called electrophoresis, depends on slight differences in the composition of hemoglobin. The apparatus used consists of an electromagnetic field. In such a field molecules of different size move at different speeds, and sickle-cell hemoglobin migrates at a slightly different rate from the hemoglobin normally found in adult man. This rate variation is caused by a difference in only one amino acid out of nine in only one of the 30 different

Fig. 15-2. Sickle-shaped red cells from a case of homozygous sickle-cell anemia (*left*) and from a heterozygous sickle-cell trait (*right*.) (From Ronald Singer,"The Sickle Cell Trait in Africa," *American Anthropologist, 55* (635), 1953. Courtesy of the author and the journal.)

peptides of which a molecule of hemoglobin is composed. In every other respect normal and sickle-cell hemoglobin are identical, yet when enough of the hemoglobin has this one slight difference, the red cells lose their shape and clog the fine blood vessels, where they are rapidly destroyed. This produces the anemia. In patients with the anemia only the sickle-cell type of hemoglobin occurs, but in heterozygous sicklers there is also a variable amount of normal hemoglobin. Cells containing this mixture ordinarily maintain their shape in the blood vessels.

Using one or another of the tests, it has been observed that sickling is frequent in places where malaria is common. A. C. Allison (1954), a physician studying this condition in East Africa, discovered that heterozygous individuals are apparently much more immune to malaria than are homozygous "normals." A double natural selection is at work here: a selection against homozygous sicklers, many of whom die of anemia and hence fail to reproduce and, in the tropics, a selection against homozygous "normals," many of whom die of malaria. The biological price of maintaining many heterozygous individuals in the population, however, is the birth of numerous homozygotes of both types. These types are not equal in numbers: The selective pressure against sickle-cell anemia is more extreme than that against susceptibility to malaria. But there is some point, an equilibrium, where the pressures will be in balance. This point will be different in different places, depending on the prevalence of malaria; and hence even at equilibrium the frequency of the sickle-cell gene will vary from place to place. This may account in large part for the great racial differences in the frequency of this characteristic: as much as 40 per cent or more in some parts of Africa, nearly 10 per cent in American Negroes, but virtually none in large parts of Europe and Asia (it does occur in some parts of India, Turkey, and Greece).

Another mechanism may in part explain the distribution of sickling. The heterozygous sicklers, like the homozygous, though to a much lesser extent, show a tendency to anemia. Anemic persons are at a special disadvantage at high elevations because the rarefied atmosphere, hence sparsity of oxygen, is imposed on a biological system already deficient in its capacity to transport oxygen from the lungs to the body tissues. Sickling would therefore be more rigorously eliminated by natural selection the higher the elevation. It also happens in many places that malarial mosquitos are unable to live at higher altitudes. If direct altitude effects are important in determining the distribution of the sickling gene they would therefore show a distribution pattern much like that of a selection involving malaria. Both explanations are consistent with the low frequency of sickling among the Nilgiri Hills people of India, the highlanders of Central Africa, and the mountain Berbers farther north.

A Similar Case, Thalassemia

Another anemia, *thalassemia,* also has a peculiar distribution. First described in 1925 by Dr. Thomas B. Cooley, a Detroit physician, and his assistant, Pearl Lee, Cooley's disease (as it is also called) is most common in malarious parts of the Mediterranean basin (whence the third alternative name, Mediterranean anemia). Regions where malaria is common, such as the Po

Valley in Italy and, until recently, the island of Sardinia, have a high incidence of thalassemia. A group of Italian hemotologists (Carcassi *et al.*, 1957) proposed to study the condition as Allison had done with the sickle cell trait in Africa—by inoculating individuals of various genetic types with malaria, studying their immunity, and then curing those who were not immune with atabrin or other antimalarial drugs. Since the advent of DDT, Sardinia has been freed of malaria, and the authorities have refused the request. "We have just rid the island of malaria," they said, "and now you propose to bring it back." The research team was able to demonstrate, however, that a test of the heterozygotes of thalassemia shows positive in 19 percent and 21 percent of individuals in two Sardinian villages in a low valley, but in only 4 percent and 5 percent in two other nearby villages in the hills. This difference could hardly be due to a genetically distinct immigrant population because the frequencies of the Rh and MNS blood groups were similar in all four towns; those of the ABO blood groups were as different between the two mountain towns and between the two valley towns as between the two zones of altitude. This points to the possible effect of malaria as a selective agent in thalassemia, as the hill towns have always been relatively free of malaria, but it was formerly common in the valley towns. The authors did not study the possibility of adverse effects of red cell fragility, the condition they equated with heterozygous thalassemia, on survival at higher elevations, however.

Electrophoretic tests of the blood from patients with thalassemia reveal that the hemoglobin is almost entirely of a type normally found only in the fetus and newborn. The disease apparently prevents the formation of the normal amount of adult hemoglobin.

Electrophoretic tests have also revealed a number of other abnormal hemoglobins (C, D, E, G, H, I, J, K, and M), each of which also migrates at its own specific rate in an electrophoretic field. Anemia is often found in individuals heterozygous for the genes responsible for one of these abnormalities and also heterozygous for the sickle-cell condition or for thalassemia. The same is true of individuals homozygous for hemoglobin C or E. The gene for hemoglobin C is most common in West Africa, where the sickle-cell trait is rare; those for hemoglobins E and H are common in

Thailand, where thalassemia is also common. All the abnormal hemoglobins occur principally in regions of endemic malaria.

Primaquine Sensitivity

One further property of the blood of some individuals, only now under thorough study and still only partially understood, may help show the interrelationship between physical anthropology—with its interests in ongoing natural selection—and clinical medicine. When certain drugs and even one important food, the fava bean, are ingested, a small proportion of individuals suffer from an acute anemia in which the red blood cells are destroyed. This condition is called *primaquine sensitivity* because the nature of the red cell anomaly responsible for the anemia and a laboratory test for the sensitivity were first worked out in connection with studies of the antimalarial drug primaquine (Beutler, 1959).

Among British troops receiving the drug no reactions were noted, but there were frequent cases in Asiatic Indian and Burmese troops. Later it was shown that white Americans rarely show the sensitivity, but that many American Negroes do. Some 10 percent of Negroes, Asiatic Indians, and Chinese (including those from Formosa) show the sensitivity, but it occurs in less than 1 percent in Europeans, one group of American Indians, and two African groups, Sudanese and Bedouins. A test-tube test for the sensitivity to the drug also reveals many positives in American Negroes, some in Orientals, and few in most Caucasian groups. None of a series of Ashkenazic (north and east European) Jews showed the sensitivity, but there are cases in Jews from Turkey, Bulgaria, Iraq, Yemen, North Africa, and Persia. The geographic distribution of persons with the red cell defect corresponds to areas of endemic malaria (Motulsky, 1960). One may well speculate that another mechanism of resistance to malaria is involved here.

Primaquine sensitivity clearly runs in families. Some tests on females, but none in males, give intermediate results. This suggests that heterozygotes occur only in females and that the condition depends on a sex-linked gene on the X chromosome. Primaquine sensitivity may thus afford an opportunity to calculate natural selection pressures of a sex-linked gene.

Selection in the Case of Erythro-blastosis Fetalis

Just as there are cases of selection against homozygotes, there may be selection against heterozygotes. An example of this kind is found in the disease *erythroblastosis fetalis,* a condition usually apparent soon after birth. It is characterized by an excessive destruction of red blood cells and a compensatory overdevelopment of those tissues in which red blood cells are formed. The skin may have a yellowish color, and the liver and spleen are enlarged.

The disease is usually due to a difference in Rh blood type between the mother and her infant, such as occurred in the case reported by Levine and Stetson discussed in Chapter 14. The various subtypes of the Rh factor are all inherited as dominants over the Rh-negative condition. Ordinarily the Rh substances produce no untoward reactions during blood transfusions or in any other way. However, an Rh-negative woman can be sensitized against the Rh substances by receiving Rh-positive blood transfusions. This works something like immunity to infectious disease: Presence of Rh substance produces, in the serum, antibodies inimical to itself. Such resistance is a healthy attribute in terms of disease; in the case of Rh antibodies, however, the mother can bear Rh-positive children, yet their red blood cells can be destroyed by their mother's antibodies. Erythroblastosis fetalis occurs, therefore, in Rh-positive children of Rh-negative women. In these cases the father is Rh-positive since the positive condition is dominant and can be transmitted by the father even when the mother is negative.

Another way in which an Rh-negative woman may become sensitized is from an Rh-positive fetus in her womb. Fetal blood does not cross the placenta to flow in the mother's veins, but some antigen must cross because Rh substances in the fetal red blood cells are able to produce antibodies in the mother's blood serum. The antibodies thus built up in the mother may then be carried in her serum to a subsequent Rh-positive fetus where they react with the red cells to the detriment of the fetus. A peculiar feature of this mother-child incompatibility is that erythroblastosis fetalis apparently occurs less often when mother and father are of different

ABO blood groups. It has recently been suggested that, contrary to previous ideas on the subject, fetal red cells find their way into the maternal circulation. When such fetal cells are of a different ABO group than those of the mother, they would be rapidly inactivated, according to this view, and the fetal cells would have less time to stimulate the production of Rh antibodies in the mother's blood serum (Levine, 1958). Incompatibility in the ABO system seems to reduce the likelihood of erythroblastosis caused by the development of Rh antibodies in the mother.

Erythroblastosis fetalis is now treated successfully, by gradually replacing all the newborn infant's bood by transfusion. In former times there were many deaths, however, all of them among heterozygous infants. Every such death removed an equal number of Rh-negative and Rh-positive genes from the population, since the child must have inherited an Rh-negative gene from its negative mother, yet must have had the Rh-positive allele to manifest the disease. Polymorphism in such a case would not be balanced; it would be unstable and one or the other homozygotic type would tend to become universal in the population.

If we started with just 50 percent of genes of each kind, the ratio would not change. But if we assume 50 people carrying 82 Rh-positive genes and 18 (18 percent) Rh-negative genes, then the death of 10 heterozygotes would leave 72 Rh-positive and 8 (11 percent) Rh-negative. The relative frequency would thus have changed appreciably. Even with just 50 percent of each type of gene, the equilibrium would be unstable. Any deviation for any reason would set in motion a process leading to further changes in the same direction. We would expect one or the other homozygous type soon to be naturally selected. How then does it happen that many human groups retain both the dominant and the recessive alleles? Frankly, we do not know. Perhaps there are some still unknown advantages in heterozygosis, just as the sickle-cell disease was an enigma until the role of resistance to malaria was suggested.

GENERAL REFERENCES

Dobzhansky, Th., 1951, *Genetics and the Origin of the Species,* 3d ed,. revised. New York: Columbia University Press. A genetic interpretation of evolutionary mechanisms from the neo-Darwinian point of view. See especially Chapter 1, "Organic Diversity," Chapter 5, "Adaptive Polymorphism," and Chapter 10, "Patterns of Evolution."

Wallace, Bruce, and Th. Dobzhansky, 1959, *Radiation, Genes, and Man.* New York: Holt, Rinehart and Winston, Inc. Describes the role of mutation among the factors affecting genetic human changes.

16. Some Further Factors in the Population Genetics of Raciation

Climate and the Fitness of Races

We are most certain about the role played by natural selection in respect to human traits that are either nearly universal or extraordinarily rare in the species; that is, the genes responsible for normal development of sight, hearing, growth, and so on, and those determining major impairments: blindness, deafness, dwarfism, and the like. This situation has not prevented considerable speculation concerning almost every human racial trait, however. Professor Carlton Coon of the University of Pennsylvania, one of the foremost students of the races of Europe and the Middle East, and his associates have argued that differences in body shape in the races of various parts of the world are related to climatic differences (Coon, Garn and Birdsell, 1950; Coon, 1959). This line of reasoning has been pressed by others also, especially with regard to extreme climatic regions and their peoples: the Eskimos, the Australian aborigines, and tropical Africans.

Certain facts about the human body have been worked into a theory of natural selection of racial traits. Heat produced by the human body is the result of chemical activity within cells, a physiological activity called metabolism. Metabolism, in turn, is more or less proportional to the number or volume of such cells—that is, the amount of metabolizing tissue. On the other hand, loss of heat occurs at the skin and is roughly proportional to the surface area

171

of the body. Despite the fact that not all tissue metabolizes equally and that heat is lost also from exhaled air, it is generally true that people with a small surface in relation to their weight tend to conserve heat while those with a relatively large surface area cool off more readily. Advocates of the theory point out that Eskimos are heavy for their height (and hence for their surface area) whereas the reverse is true of some of the desert peoples. The situation is actually much more complex, however, as the proponents of the theory themselves recognize. For example, of two persons of identical body build but different size, the bigger person would weigh relatively more for each square inch of skin area. In countries like China, with some degree of intermarriage between regions, the people of the more northern and colder provinces are larger than those of the warmer south. The same is true to a small extent of the white population of the 48 contiguous states of the United States. On the other hand, the Eskimos are small people, whereas some inhabitants of the borders of the Sahara, for instance, tend to be large.

In order to relate body build to climate we shall have to abandon simple assumptions and accept the probability of complex size and shape factors sometimes operating in opposite directions. For example, increased size in man is ordinarily achieved by a disproportional growth of the limbs compared to that of the trunk; tall men tend to be linear while short men tend to be compact. To this extent, the size and shape principles counteract each other, and the body weight per square inch of skin surface tends to be stable. This relation between shape, size, and weight has not been accurately measured in most groups, and we do not know whether the weight for a unit of surface is greater in Eskimos than it is in Arabs. If the ratio of weight to surface area were found to be higher in the offspring of Arctic than of desert peoples brought up together in New York, for instance, we could ascribe the differences in physique to inheritance and could postulate that they resulted from differential natural selection of their forebearers in different climates.

Adaptive advantage must be viewed as a complicated equilibrium between a large number of factors. On the desert there is a need for water conservation, for instance; but the conservation of body water would require the same compact "arctic" body type that effectively conserves heat. If we reach the conclusion that heat conservation is more important, based on the knowledge that Eskimos are small and compact whereas desert people are tall and linear, we cannot then use these facts as evidence for the theory of "fitness" of racial types. That would be a circular argument. Furthermore, peoples of quite different physical characteristics sometimes live close to each other. In Central Africa short squat pygmies live near full-size Bantus; and the Watusis, one of the tallest, lankiest people in the world, live not far away. During his voyage on the *Beagle*, Darwin saw some nearly naked natives on the shore of the cold barren island of Tierra del Fuego, at the southernmost tip of South America. If he had known then that one aboriginal group, the Yahgan, are, on the average, extremely short, while another, the Ona, living in much the same way, on the same island, are tall—how would he have explained the situation as survival of the fittest?

One possible answer is that one or the other of the groups evolved elsewhere and migrated into the region relatively recently. But in this and other similar cases we have no direct knowledge of such migrations. It seems to me that there is no compelling evidence for natural selection in every racial difference. After the fact one may argue that this or that attribute of physique must be good for this or that climate, and a reasonable picture can be drawn. Such a picture, however, starts with the assumption of the theory of natural selection of racial characteristics; it does little to support such a theory so long as equally possible alternative explanations remain untested. Factors in cultural history, such as the development of clothes, weapons, or means of exploiting the environment, may be the chief influences in the distribution of races. The arguments concerning racial differences as natural fitness for one or another environment are interesting, even plausible; but, for the most part, scientists must still label them as "undemonstrated."

Random Genetic Drift

Random genetic drift is the third of the four main ways by which changes in gene frequency are explained. If mutation and natural selection do not adequately account for human evolution, what else could be involved? One suggestion is that, in part, it may be explained by chance. This explanation seems a contradiction in terms: Saying that changes are due to chance seems to be saying that they are not explained. What is implied in this case, however, is merely selection of some genetic factors for increase or decrease on the basis of causes unrelated to biology, causes that can be understood only by the history of particular events. Thus, if an old man on crossing a street corner, and being rather slow about it, is knocked over by an errand boy on a bicycle who observed the traffic light but not the traffic, the incident is "accidental" as far as the law is concerned. The policeman who hurries to the scene is not concerned with the reason why either the man or the boy should be passing just that particular spot just at that time. In the same way, factors of no appreciable pertinence to genetics may modify gene frequencies. To that extent, chance may be said to explain changes in gene frequencies, although this does not preclude a complete explanation if it were possible and worthwhile to ascertain all the unknown factors. The cumulative effect of haphazard variations is called *random genetic drift*.

Let us go back to the little group of 50 people we used as an example of the effects of natural selection favoring the homozygotes. We postulated the death of 10 individuals and showed that this would change the gene frequency from 18 percent to 11 percent. In a group of this size, however, if the 10 deaths occurred at random (or if 10 individuals remained unmarried and did not contribute to the next generation) it can be demonstrated statistically that a change of similar magnitude would be expected to occur about once in every 10 generations or so. Furthermore, the deviation from generation to generation may be cumulative. Sooner or later there might be a whole generation of Rh-positive or of Rh-negative individuals. Once this has happened the random drift will have "fixed" one of the genes. Thereafter all subsequent generations can only inherit the one type of gene—unless the other is reintroduced by mutation or by an immigrant.

It should be apparent that the smaller the population, the more likely are such chance fluctuations. In large groups they are not likely to be a significant factor. Sewall Wright (1938) has shown that not only is the total size of the breeding population important, but also the variability in the size of families. Obviously, if many individuals had few or no offspring, while others were the parents of many, random genetic drift would be more prevalent than if the distribution of offspring were more even. Increase in variability in family size thus has the same effect as decrease in size of the group. The term "effective size of the breeding population" is used to describe the number of parents per generation adjusted for variability in the number of offspring (Boyd, 1950).

One feature of random variation is its virtual absence in large breeding populations; in them, numerous "chance" events tend to counterbalance each other. The fact that random genetic drift is as likely to encourage unfavorable as favorable evolution has led some competent research workers to minimize its significance. Others have pointed out, however, that if a species is incompletely divided into partially isolated subpopulations, random variation would provide "pools" of genes (including some for unfavorable characteristics) that would enhance the possibility for natural selection when the requirements for survival change. Thus, a small group ill adapted to a cold climate could serve as a genetic pool of favorable traits for the whole species in a subsequent warm epoch. Wright (1932) visualized the ways of life as a map with peaks (good ways of life) and valleys (Fig. 16-1). If a species with small breeding

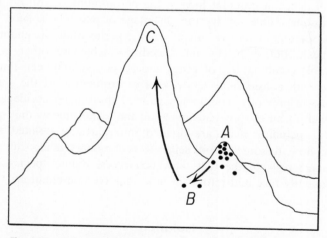

Fig. 16-1. Scheme showing adaptive peaks. A species adapted to the ecological niche represented by peak A could, by natural selection, achieve peak C if incompletely divided into relatively small subgroups that vary (by random genetic drift) so that some would first be relatively ill adapted in valley B.

populations were distributed on such a map, natural selection would attract the populations to the peaks; that is, the groups would adapt to the possible ways of life, sometimes called *ecological niches* by biologists. Random genetic drift would cause the paths to zigzag, however, and sometimes to descend. Although, to that extent, the organisms would be ill adapted, their descent would permit the groups to enter declivities from which the ascent of higher peaks might begin. In other words, a slightly ill-adapted species with a variety of subraces may be more able than a wholly successful one to exploit the environment in some strikingly new way by a radical evolutionary step. The human type of upright gait, for example, may have started with a relatively ill-adapted quadruped. Finally, the occasional interbreeding between subgroups leads to a sharing of any favorable modifications established in one of the subgroups. Such shared traits might eventually be established in the whole species if they are highly advantageous for survival.

Many important capacities seem to result from combinations of genetic traits. Just as the heterozygote for sickling may be more fit than either homozygote, so also there may be favorable combinations of genes at different loci on the chromosome or on different chromosomes. One can see the advantage of partially isolated subgroups scattered over the "map," each experimentally ascending its own peak, but then (by interbreeding) achieving other peaks. Favorable combinations of genes and genetic systems can thus be altered with considerably less risk of extermination of the species and loss of previous evolutionary gains. I think it no accident, but the result of an adaptive advantage in the arrangement, that many species, including man, are divided into partially isolated races which show, to some extent, separate evolutionary tendencies. The advantage rests in the fact that such races, unlike species, may subsequently fuse and reform in new adaptive combinations.

Isolation

The graphic model has introduced still another factor besides mutation, natural selection, and random genetic drift. Mating is selective; there is a tendency for members of subgroups of the species to mate among themselves (isolation) but occasionally to inter-breed. If the groups differ greatly in their gene frequencies, then a mate of one's own group is more likely to share one's own genetic characteristics than is a potential mate from another group. Isolation is thus one form or cause of *assortative mating*—a match in which particular characteristics of one mate tend to be associated with some special characteristics (usually similar) in the other mate. Men and women are most likely to marry persons in the same area or country; to some extent there is isolation by distance. Similarly, human beings usually marry members of their own social group—those who share the same values and speak the same language. The barrier of physical distance was surmounted in favor of social vicinity in a fairly recent case where, after repeal of the Chinese Exclusion Law and passage of the so-called "Bride's Act" of 1947, some 6000 young Chinese-Americans rushed to China to woo and marry before the right to bring Chinese-born wives to the United States expired in December, 1949. Most of the men went to the very counties where their ancestors had lived, and sought introductions through the usual family channels; they married the very girls they might have married had their fathers never left home. Assortative mating also may be a deliberate choice (sometimes no doubt sub-conscious) of mates with similar physical characteristics; despite the common supposition to the contrary, opposites do not usually attract. Assortative mating has the effect of narrowing the number of potential mates and of limiting the breeding group, hence of en-hancing the likelihood of maintaining in the group genetic differ-ences from the population at large.

Some human breeding groups are small enough for random factors to be quite pronounced. The population of the Bass Straight Islands, Australia, started with 21 adults. The 200-odd inhabitants of the little island of Tristan da Cunha in the South Atlantic are descended from eight men and seven women who settled there following the Napoleonic wars, and a few subsequent immigrants. Pitcairn Island in the Pacific was peopled by the descendants of six of the mutineers of the British ship *Bounty* and eight or nine Poly-nesian women. Bentley Glass, Professor of Biology at Johns Hop-kins University, and his associates (1952) have shown that random genetic drift actually occurs in the blood group genes in a similar-sized group in this country—one of the little religious sects, a Dunkard community in Pennsylvania. Another religious community of the United States and Canada, the Hutterites, has several separate colonies in which gene frequencies for the blood groups have drifted apart. Even in these small groups, however, there are some immigrants who came, joined the group, and had children. In the case of the Dunkard community this immigration has been at the rate of some 10 to 22 percent per generation, but even this rate did not prevent significant random fluctuation. In general, the smaller the effective population size and the smaller the immigration rate, the greater will be the random variation in gene frequencies. The effective population size multiplied by the immigration rate may be used as a measure of the degree of isolation. When it is below about 50, random drift could be a significant factor. The coefficient of breeding isolation would be well below 50 in the cases of Tristan da Cunha, Pitcairn, and the Pennsylvania Dunkards, for example. It was probably often low at various times and places in man's history and prehistory (Lasker, 1954A).

Differential Growth of Populations

Granted that little groups do come to have different gene frequencies—to evolve in various directions—how, one might ask, could this evolution result in major racial groups which, almost by definition, consist of large numbers of people? Obviously, this development would require a substantial expansion in the group through natural increase without the group losing its genetic isolation. Some anthropologists and geneticists consider such population explosion an unlikely event, and hence minimize the significance of random genetic drift. Although admitting the possibility of chance variations, they would deny its importance. I believe, however, that in some cases unknown but specific historical influences may have led to just such rapid increases in population. If so, deviant gene frequencies that had resulted from genetic drift could have become fixed in the population of continents or other large areas of the world. For example, on a smaller scale, the people of the Bass Straight Islands, Tristan da Cunha, and Pitcairn have each multiplied more than tenfold: They crowd their little islands, despite the fact that many members of each group have emigrated (Birdsell, 1957).

Similarly, the Hutterites, members of a German religious sect who settled in the United States and Canada, increased from 443 to 8542 within 70 years (Eaton and Mayer, 1953). The conditions that led to their increase—high incidence of early marriage, group responsibility for the children, and limited personal financial requirements—are present in many peoples besides the Hutterites, and many other immigrant groups have profited from easy access to land in the United States. The Hutterites early adopted our methods of hygiene (with consequent low infant death rates) and yet, until recently, firmly rejected offsetting attitudes common in the American way of life such as late marriage and family limitation. Since the Hutterites (like the Dunkards mentioned previously) differ genetically on the average from other people about them, then the Hutterite way of life has been an historical evolutionary force.

Likewise, the enormous relative increase in the world frequency of blondness, light skin color, and blood group A_2, which presumably occurred during the centuries of European expansion, can be better understood in terms of development of machines and weapons by Europeans than in terms of the biology of pigmentation and blood (Hulse, 1955 and 1957). The reversal of the trend and the tendency of other characteristics to increase are also better understood in terms of the introduction of modern medicine in formerly backward areas than by any difference in natural fecundity.

Finally, it is not necessary to postulate a large number of instances in which populations grew inordinately. The number of major racial groups recognized is modest, albeit somewhat indeterminate (Garn and Coon, 1955). On the other hand, the number of human population isolates was undoubtedly relatively large ever since paleolithic times, and expansion of only a small fraction of them would account for the subsequent racial distributions. The remaining isolates under these circumstances would have become extinct or, more probably, would have merged after their numbers had become relatively so small that their incorporation would have had little effect.

The Significance of the World Distribution of ABO Blood Group Frequencies

Dr. Alice Brues (1954), an anthropologist who teaches anatomy at the University of Oklahoma, has shown that the world distribution of the blood groups is consistent with the thesis that natural selection is important in differentiating the human genus from all other animals, but that chance factors are more important in producing the present characteristics of human races. The ABO blood groups are so distributed among the races of man that the percentage of the I^A gene varies up to 50 percent, the I^B gene up to 35 percent, and the i gene rarely below 50 percent; in short, only about one-fourth of the possible combinations are actually to be found in various groups of man. Brues argues that this suggests natural selection acting, like vectors in a force analysis, so as to produce an equilibrium at about 25 percent gene I^A, 15 percent gene I^B, and 60 percent gene i. These forces must have been at work for very long periods of time because blood groups essentially like the human ones are also found in the anthropoid apes. It is therefore probable that the departures from this equilibrium of optimum frequencies are due to the action of random genetic drift and historical accident. Indeed, some of the most distinct blood group frequencies are found in relatively isolated peoples—for example, the Basques and the Lapps.

It is true that there are selective factors that operate through the blood groups. Persons with blood group O are more likely than others to have stomach ulcers; and there are other associations between the blood groups and disease. Some anthropologists have suggested that because certain diseases are more serious under particular climatic conditions than under others, such associations may effect racial differentiation. We have little factual evidence, however, that the selective force is significantly different in different peoples or places. The world-wide pattern of human blood group frequencies suggests that random genetic drift works at the racial or local level, causing some variation in the frequencies of genes that were already present in man's precursors. Natural selection operates at the same time, but perhaps chiefly on a species-wide scale. It tends to restore a characteristic equilibrium between the frequencies of the various blood groups, or at least to prevent the establishment of homozygous local populations all of whose members are as alike in blood groups as an inbred strain of white mice are in respect to the pink color of their eyes. At any rate, the distribution pattern of the blood groups throughout the world is consistent with the operation of both natural selection and random factors: Natural selection on a wide scale, presumably affecting the whole species; random genetic drift on a narrow scale, differentiating local breeding isolates and, through the subsequent expansion of some of the isolates, small and large racial groups.

GENERAL REFERENCES

Birdsell, Joseph B., 1953, "Some environmental cultural factors influencing the structure of Australian aboriginal populations," *American Naturalist*, 87:171–207. A discussion of the influence of population density, mean annual rainfall, and other geographic and human factors on racial distributions and changes in a subcontinent.

Garn, Stanley M., ed., 1961, *Readings on Race*. Springfield, Ill.: C. C. Thomas. Chapter 5, pages 52–115, presents four investigations and a critical essay that bear on the question of "Climate and Race."

———, 1960, *Human Races*. Springfield, Ill.: C. C. Thomas. The processes of race formation in man.

17 · The Races of the World

As we have seen, the pool of inherited characteristics of any human population changes from time to time. It follows that no race is stable. Many biologists question the value of the concept of race, and at least one anthropologist has suggested the complete suppression of the term for serious scientific discussions (Montagu, 1951). The chief reason for the attack on the notion of race is that the concept has been much abused by persons who would emphasize human differences for the sake of maintaining a superior economic and social position.

The physical appearance of an individual does reflect his origins. The West African soldier in France and the English governess in Siam can be distinguished from the people among whom they live by racial features as well as by their dress or manners. Among neighboring peoples, however, purely racial criteria are less useful. Even persons very familiar with the Far East would make many errors in sorting out Japanese from Chinese according to purely biological criteria. Racial traits are of no use in distinguishing among French, German, English, and Irish individuals. Although, on the average, European nationalities differ slightly from one another in most racial characteristics, individuals within each of these countries vary much more. In selecting agents for espionage within each other's boundaries European countries never have needed to pay much attention to racial traits.

Men differ from each other, of course, and some differences can be called "racial." The difficulty is that all individuals differ from all others, if a wide enough variety of characteristics is considered.

Even within a single nation, tribe, or limited breeding population there are usually many differences in the color of the skin, eyes, and hair, the form of the head and face, the shape of the nose, the quantity of beard and body hair, and the proportions of the body. In some cases, however, the same criteria that separate some human groups may unite others: Skin color, for example, distinguishes all but a very few Europeans from all but a very few Negroes, but not various peoples of Oceania, the Far East, the Near East, North Africa, and the Americas from each other—although these groups may be distinguished on other grounds.

These considerations lead me to use the word "race" rarely and then chiefly to describe population entities of past times when there was somewhat less human migration and mixture. It is true that some problems of historic interpretation concerning the origins and movements of peoples cannot be solved solely by genetic analysis. Biological traits that distinguish some geographic groups, or that predominate in some groups more than in others, may be useful in reconstructing the history of populations. It is often advantageous to apply the adjective "racial" even though there be no discrete boundaries to any category to which one can apply the noun "race." Racial characteristics are certainly genetic entities, although the mechanism of their inheritance is not always fully known and, as will be shown in the next chapter, they may be modified by nongenetic influences. With each new trait that is subjected to satisfactory genetic analysis, an added fraction of human difference can be removed from the class of a purely superficial phenotypic difference and added to our store of material for analytic anthropology. The need to rely on the somewhat misleading classification of whole individuals into races thus diminishes as we increasingly use the methods of population genetics especially in the study of the processes of human differentiation. Nevertheless, an understanding of the historical development of the race concept and a brief description of the peoples of the world in respect to their racial characteristics will probably continue to serve as a background for more analytic studies of human differences.

The first serious attempts to classify the races of the world usually listed one for each of the major land masses. They agree, as do virtually all more modern classifications also, in centering one of the major races in Europe, another in Africa, and a third in East Asia. Some authorities added a fourth for America, and there was later disagreement on whether to add as separate groups the Australian Aboriginals, the Bushmen and Hottentots of South Africa, and the Pygmies. The peoples of India and the Pacific islands remained difficult to classify in such a scheme, and there was a tendency to increase the number of races.

There also was disagreement on the key characteristics of each race. One scheme used skin color (white, black, yellow, red, and brown races); another emphasized hair form; most relied on a series of readily observed traits, usually including pigment, hair, and superficial features such as head and face form and body size. Thus the Negroid is characterized as having dark brown skin, black woolly or frizzly hair, broad flat nose, and thick lips. The Mongoloid is defined by another series of characters: coarse black straight head hair, scant beard, broad flat face with projecting cheeks, a fold more or less completely covering the free margin of the eyelid (called *epicanthic* or *Mongoloid* fold; see Fig. 17-1) that gives the slitlike almond-eyed appearance, and special features of the teeth such as pronouncedly shovel-shaped incisors. A third major race is often

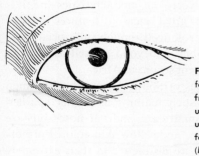

Fig. 17-1. Epicanthic or mongoloid fold (*above*). The inner portion of the free eyelash bearing margin of the upper lid, and sometimes the whole upper margin, is overhung by a thick fold of skin. In non-Mongoloid peoples (*below*) the fold is thin and less developed and, although especially in older persons it may cover the lateral and middle portion of the lid, it rarely covers the inner part.

called "Caucasoid," because of the erroneous notion that its members originated in the Caucasus Mountains. The alternatives "European" or "Europoid" are also poor terms for a race with ancient branches in Western Asia and North Africa as well as Europe. The Caucasoids are characterized as having light skin, variable hair and eye color, and relatively high narrow noses. Although any racial taxonomy is relatively artificial and arbitrary, we include a brief description following, in general, Hooton's (1946) schema.

The Negroids

The largest concentration of Negroids is found in Africa south of the Sahara Desert. The Forest Negroes of Central Africa and adjacent areas of the west coast are people of moderate size with long arms, especially in comparison with the legs, jutting (prognathous) jaws, and the woolly hair, dark skin, and other characteristics that we think of as most typically Negroid. In the Nile drainage area one finds taller, very dark Nilotic Negroes with facial features somewhat less dissimilar to those of Caucasoids. Further east in the horn of Africa and southward, Negroidal characteristics are less common, and the convergence toward Caucasoid features is more noticeable—perhaps because of prolonged though only occasional intermarriage with people of Arabia or beyond as well as because of the influence of less Negroid ancient strains in Africa.

Some apparently ancient peoples of South Africa, the Bushmen and Hottentots, are Negroid in such features as highly spiraled "peppercorn" hair (Fig. 17-2), small ears, and flat noses but are almost Mongoloid in flatness of face and sallow skin color. Furthermore, these South African groups are distinctive in their extremely short average stature, the unusual amount of fat on the buttocks and thighs of otherwise slim individuals—especially women—and some anatomical details of the reproductive organs including elongation of the labia minora (which are not entirely genetic, however, as some authors say they are deliberately stretched). Bushmen and Hottentot languages are unlike any others in the world. This fact and the primitive way of life of the Bushmen of the Kalahari Desert

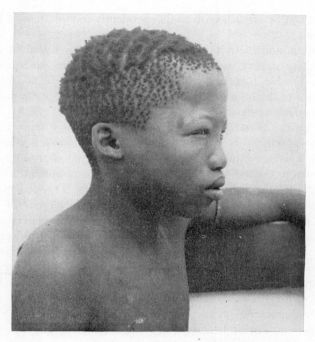

Fig. 17-2. "Peppercorn" hair of a young Bushman from Central Kalahari, Africa. (Courtesy of Martin Gusinde.)

suggest that these groups have been relatively isolated from other peoples for a long period of time.

The pygmy Negritos of Africa show some similarities to those of Oceania. Both resemble the Bushmen in being very small and not as dark as Forest Negroes. In both, the head is frequently bulging and is sometimes described as pedomorphic in form because of the small facial features. Negritos of the Congo forest show some similarities to Negroes of the same region; those of the Andaman Islands, the Malay Peninsula, interior New Guinea, and other Oceanic islands are more similar to surrounding Eastern peoples.

The larger dark-skinned Oceanic Negroids, the Melanesians and Papuans, often have less woolly and lighter colored hair, less prognathism, more prominent noses, and more body and beard hair than the African Negroids. Anthropologists do not know whether

Negroid characteristics evolved independently in two areas of tropical forests.

Negroids and their mixed descendants are also found in many areas where slavery was once rampant, such as the Americas and Arabia. The Negroids of the United States, the Caribbean area, and Brazil, for example, are, in general, attenuated types predominantly of West African origin.

Among the blood groups, one, Rh^o of the Rh system, is very common in African Negroids compared with its occurrence in other peoples. The Henshaw (He) and Hunter (Hu) blood groups, which are related to the MN system, are also found predominantly among Negroids. The gene for sickle-cell hemoglobin (s) occurs with maximum frequency in some groups of Forest Negroes of West Africa, the Congo, and East Africa; it varies locally, however, and is absent in all Oceanic Negroids so far studied; in Africa it decreases rapidly in frequency as one proceeds south among the Bantus or north in the Sudan. Hemoglobin C has a center in West Africa, being frequent in Liberia where sickling is rare. In general, the blood groups of pygmies resemble those of nearby peoples. In blood group frequencies African pygmies are distinct from those of the Andaman and Pacific Islands, except for the high frequency of Rh^o in both (Graydon and others, 1958).

The Mongoloids

The name "Mongoloid" suggests that the most representative members of the race are the Mongols. While it is true that some Mongols, Tibetans, Northern Chinese, Koreans, and Japanese fit the description, the populations which fit it best are several tribal groups of Eastern Siberia and Manchuria: Goldi, Giliak, and Koriak. Still farther to the north, in the Arctic, similar characteristics are found, although head form is relatively narrower (dolichocephalic). The Eskimos extending along the Arctic shore of America and the coasts of Greenland are big-jawed, dolichocephalic Mongoloids.

As one proceeds south in China and beyond, the average stature decreases, and the characteristic Mongoloid features are often modified or absent. The peoples of Thailand, Burma, Indochina, Malaya, and the Indonesian Islands may be thought of as belonging to the

Mongoloid race, but have dark skin, occasionally wavy hair, and less pronounced facial features than are seen in the Mongoloids of northeast Asia.

The native peoples of the Americas, the Amerindians, are Mongoloid in most respects. The hair is straight and black, the beard and body hair sparse, the face is large and broad, and the teeth usually display such Mongoloid features as the ridges that make the incisors shovel shaped. Indians from various parts of the Americas vary considerably: The nose is often more prominent and the eyes correspondingly more deeply set under well-developed brow ridges than one finds in East Asians. The contrast in features between the Indians and Eskimos of Alaska, the accumulating evidence of the antiquity of man in the New World, and the variations in degree of similarity between Old World and New World Mongoloids all point to continuing evolution within the race since man first reached America from Asia.

In respect to the blood groups, the Mongoloids show a relatively high incidence of the rare gene Rh^z, and they are low in the Rh-negative gene and in A_2, a subgroup of A. Type B, however, which reaches a maximum in Asiatic Mongoloids, is lacking or virtually so in unmixed American Indians. In America the A_1 gene varies from total absence in many tribal groups to the highest figures anywhere in the world among the Blackfoot Indians. One blood group entity, Diego (Di^a), shows up in at least moderate frequencies in most tribes of American Indians and is also found in Asiatic Mongoloids, but does not occur in any other groups so far tested (Layrisse, 1958). Another genetic trait, the inability to taste phenylthiourea, is rarer in Mongoloids than in other peoples studied. One of the abnormal hemoglobins, E, occurs in most parts of the Malayo-Indonesian area and in the Veddas of Ceylon but is lacking in other groups tested (Neel, 1957). Indeed, abnormal hemoglobins are essentially unknown among American Indians and Eskimos. Some Chinese have thalassemia (Cooley's anemia), however.

The Caucasoids

The Caucasoid, white, or "European" race is varied. Some students of the subject refer to three subdivisions: Nordic, Mediterranean, and Alpine. The Nordics are characterized as tall, blond, of long head, face, and nose; the Mediterranean as short and brunet but of similar head, face, and nose shape; and the Alpines as short but with round head, flat face, and wider nose.

Actually there are many other combinations of characters in essentially light-complexioned peoples of Europe and nearby parts of Asia and Africa; both Hooton (1946) and Coon (1939) recognize ten or more subtypes. These are of little use, it seems to me, because several or all of the types are found in every part of Europe and, moreover, on the basis of such fine subdivisions, children frequently would not belong to the same "race" as either parent. As demonstrated in a study of the races of Ireland (Hunt, 1959), the distribution of racial types is almost what one would expect if the various characteristics ascribed to race (such as eye color, hair form, head shape) are distributed independently of each other.

In respect to specific genetic traits, the Caucasoids are marked by the highest proportions of persons who cannot taste phenylthiourea, the maximum frequencies of Rh-negative, rh^1, and A_2. Also, the further west in Europe one goes, the lower is the frequency of blood group B.

There remain several large areas of the world inhabited by people of brunet or darker complexion but with features of the head and face similar to those of Europeans.

The Ainu of the northern islands of Japan are characterized by the abundance of beard and body hair—exceeding in this respect even "Alpine" Europeans. They also have notably large jaws and teeth. In other respects they either converge toward Caucasoid (as in skin color) or toward Mongoloid (in facial features and high proportion of blood group B). The Mongoloid features of the Ainu are ascribed by most anthropologists to mixture with Japanese neighbors, some of which is known to have occurred in recent times.

The peoples of the Indian Peninsula and Ceylon, the Indo-Dravidians, are distinguished from other Caucasoids (especially the Mediterranean type) only by the usually darker pigmentation, small size, and delicate skeleton. The peoples of the subcontinent are varied, of course. In India, dominant groups, composed for the most part of offspring of immigrant invaders of distinct racial affinities, have sought to maintain a position superior to that of aboriginal and other older groups through the institution of endogamous castes whose members are constrained to mate only among themselves. Such castes were, no doubt, sometimes racially different to begin with and also constitute socially isolated small populations within which further differentiation by random genetic drift is likely to have occurred (Sanghvi and Khanolkar, 1949). In general, the Indo-Dravidians are higher in blood groups M and B than the peoples of Europe.

The Polynesians, the native peoples of the outer islands of the Pacific from New Zealand to Hawaii and from Samoa to Easter Island, are difficult to classify. They are usually large, brown-skinned people with large face and head and wavy hair. The Polynesians are not extreme in the color or contours that define any major race. Hooton considers them predominantly white; Heyerdahl believes that they drifted in rafts from South America. Still another fanciful view is that they descended from partly European and partly Arabian mariners of Alexander the Great's defeated navy who diffused over the South Pacific. In my view none of these claims is based on satisfactory evidence. There is no direct evidence concerning the origins of the Polynesians. The earliest known evidence of habitation in Polynesia is about 126 B.C. Despite the lack of evident close relationships between the Polynesians and the peoples of the islands closer to Asia (Micronesia, Melanesia, Indonesia, and Australia), some physical features and the lack of the Diego blood group relate the Polynesians in this direction rather than with the New World. The low incidence of blood groups N and B of the inhabitants of some Polynesian islands cause some students of blood groups to postulate a relationship with South America, however (Simmons and Graydon, 1957).

The Australian aborigines are marked by brown skin, usually wavy dark brown hair, narrow heads, short protruding prognathic faces, large jaws and teeth, receding chin, and very large brow ridges. Birdsell has stressed that the Australian aborigines are of three distinct types, but to some anthropologists, including me, the diversity is less striking than it is in many other areas, and the skull form is consistent enough so that an experienced physical anthropologist will recognize most Australian skulls for what they are. Nevertheless, it is true that the aborigines of Tasmania were small men with almost woolly hair, whereas in southern Australia there are big-boned, hairy, almost Caucasoid individuals, and in the north there is a history (and evidence) of contact with New Guinea. Except in the north, blood group B is lacking in Australia and group M is infrequent (as also in the somewhat similar appearing Ainu).

Subraces

The racial groups described above are often further subdivided, either in terms of geographic distribution or finer definition of the type. There are drawbacks to both bases, however. If a race is subdivided into geographic subraces, the individual members cannot all be correctly ascribed to their subrace on the basis of physical characteristics alone. That is, if we describe a Malay subrace of the Indo-Malayan branch of Mongoloids we shall find some Malayans who cannot be ascribed with certainty to this subrace on the basis of appearance, and we shall find outside the area, among American Indians or Chinese, perhaps, individuals who cannot be excluded from the Malayan subrace on the basis of appearance. Alternatively, when subraces are defined entirely in terms of appearance, every part of the world (indeed, most communities and even many families) will contain individuals who, by definition, belong to different subraces.

Geographical subraces can be defined in statistical terms. The physical features, average measurements, and frequency of blood groups can be specified for a random sample of, say, Hopi Indians and these can be compared with similar data for Navaho and Apache Indians.

Alternatively (but less efficiently, I believe), one can compare the relative frequency of morphological types. Such types are segregated on the basis of a number of different distinguishing features. Morphological types may have arbitrary names (A, B, and C) or names suggesting local distribution (Pueblo, Forest, Plains) or names drawn from nearby or distant tribes and peoples. Hooton (1930), for example, described eight types among the skulls of the Indians of the prehistoric Pecos Pueblo, and by tracing the changes in proportion of the eight types from period to period he outlined the history of its people in terms of their morphological type.

I believe that the utilization of either system of forming subraces rests on the assumption that races evolved long ago and under circumstances that no longer hold true. If, as already indicated, evolution within races and smaller groups continues, then differentiation, convergence, and mixture may all play a part in modifying local groups. For this reason I prefer to deal with the local breeding group for what it is and to study the distribution within such groups of *racial traits* rather than the distribution of races as such. In this way, I believe, we can make some inroads into the analysis of the biological origins of peoples. So many theories have been advanced for the racial origin of most peoples that we are faced with the difficulty of determining the correct theory. Who are the Irish; where did the Papuans of New Guinea come from; what are the components of the people of Madagascar? There seems to be an overabundance of answers. Racial typologies tend to give an overprecise answer when all that is possible is an outline for study.

In the early stage of anthropology racial typology afforded a first crude framework for the study of the biological history of peoples. Today we would do better to analyze the various characteristics one by one, study the way they are inherited, and give a more cautious and scientific evaluation of the state of our knowledge. A map of the world or some area of it in which the frequency of different independently inherited traits are superimposed on each other would indicate the biological similarities of man. In many cases, where subsequent changes are not too numerous or profound, it would point to historic common origins. To this extent we shall heed the evidence of past studies of race: No single characteristic can indicate racial origins or population movements, and we need not assign each individual to a race to study these problems. The trait distributions themselves should prove more helpful.

Microgeographical Races and Breeding Populations

Trait distributions can only be plotted by first counting the frequencies in populations. We are therefore still faced with the necessity of determining the boundaries of natural groupings of human beings. When such groupings are inferred from the presence of natural geographic boundaries they are called *microgeographical races.* The term is sometimes extended to other small local groups. Since the crux of the matter is who breeds with whom, I prefer to speak of these groups of people as *breeding populations.* Of course, the question of past practices in mate selection can often be inferred only from the present distribution of cultural attributes. Under primitive conditions tribes tended to stay relatively isolated from each other in the genetic sense, primarily because of the inability of members to understand each other's languages. In agricultural societies, attachment of peasants to the soil often leads to mating within the community or with a person born and living within an hour or two's walk. As we have already noted, religion or caste may lead to subdivision of the population of a single area into several almost separate breeding populations.

Even in large mobile populations it is possible to record the distances between the birthplace of mates or to estimate the probable size of the breeding isolate from the frequency of marriages between first cousins or individuals of other degrees of relationship. In such places the anthropologist may be reduced to sampling more or less arbitrary geographic areas for his racial studies.

Some of the processes of race formation may well take place in the larger arena of major climatic zones; others are possible only in the population isolate. In any case, the process of ongoing human evolution can best be studied if the unit of analysis is the natural breeding population—ordinarily the local community or group.

The major races, then, are largely abstractions. It is true that they probably reflect something of the past movements and locations of peoples. But human change has been so complex that the major races serve merely as formal pedagogical categories into which the peoples of the world can be roughly sorted. It seems unlikely that such a classification can produce significant new insights into human prehistory. Sorting into primary races has historical significance, however, as the first crude method by which anthropologists began the study of race. Physical anthropology is now embarked on a finer analysis in which the natural unit is the breeding population.

The Question of Racial Differences in Mentality

The Europeans who first saw peoples of different races in far-off places also noted that these peoples had different ways of life. In general, these ways of life seemed to the European observer to be inferior to his own. Europeans with an interest in subjugating foreign lands or enslaving their peoples found it gratifying to find proof, as they deceived themselves into thinking, that the natives were mentally inferior and incapable of governing themselves. Such arguments, bolstered by the economic and psychological interests of the protagonist, persist even when unfounded. The recurrence of this kind of racism in Nazi Germany should warn us of the virulence of the fallacy. Nazi race theoreticians had to develop a racial theory that would place the Japanese in the same category as the Germans yet justify the virtual extermination of the Jews as "unfit." The hold that this and similar nonsense may achieve can best be understood in terms of first, the political manipulation of racial symbols by an unscrupulous demagogue such as Hitler and, second, people's psychological willingness to believe it.

Serious students of race have long tried to deal with race and capacity separately and to see whether there are, in fact, any racial differences in mental capacities. Concerning their findings, two excerpts from the "Statement on Race" of a distinguished committee of scientists assembled by the United Nations Educational, Scientific and Cultural Organization (UNESCO) are valuable. They write (Shapiro, 1952):

> Available scientific knowledge provides no basis for believing that the groups of mankind differ in their innate capacity for intellectual and emotional development.

Further, there is no known biological impediment to race mixture:

> The evidence points to the fact that human hybridization has been going on for an indefinite but considerable time. Indeed, one of the processes of race formation and race extinction or absorption is by means of hybridization between races. As there is no reliable evidence that disadvantageous effects are produced thereby, no biological justification exists for prohibiting intermarriage between persons of different races.

It is true, of course, that persons of different nationality, language, or religion may respond quite differently to the same event or circumstance. Nationality, language, and religion, however, are facets of culture that are learned by individuals. Within a cultural group exposed to similar cultural stimuli, psychologists may identify differences in mental capacity or temperament that are presumably innate. But between individuals of different culture, hence with different aspirations and habits of thought and speech, there is no satisfactory way to measure innate intelligence. One can say, therefore, that all groups seem to have some bright and some dull individuals but that if group differences in innate capacity exist, they have not been demonstrated under conditions of identical or equivalent culture. Even with members of a Stone Age culture, the Australian aborigines, tests in which the importance of language is minimized show that when the unfamiliarity with the test situation is taken into account, the aborigines' response is generally little if at all inferior to that of whites. In tests scored on speed or memory their performance is poor, presumably because the tests are not relevant to the aborigines' culture and experience.

Tests of American Negroes and whites show many Negroes scoring higher than some whites and some Negroes higher than most whites, although the whites usually have a slightly higher average score. In view of the wide differences in educational opportunities, these scoring differences cannot be considered proof of an inherent superiority. On the contrary, Klineberg (1935), in a series of studies of Negro children born in the South but living in New York City, showed that success in intelligence tests was greater the longer the children had been in New York. Klineberg also analyzed the school records of Negroes in the South and showed that those who later migrated did no better in school than those who stayed behind. Thus the better scores of Northern than Southern Negroes is not a matter of selection; young Negroes who later went North were no brighter than their schoolmates in the South. The later improvement in their ability with intelligence tests reflects some aspect of the changed circumstances of their life. Other studies also demonstrate that native intelligence is not adequately measured by tests; test scores can be modified by sociocultural conditions.

We know that mental and physiological functions are dependent on biological structure, but there is no evidence that those particular structural differences we observe to distinguish races have anything to do with intelligence. Evidence of racial differences in simpler physiological functions are largely subject to the same criticism: We lack proof that cultural and environmental factors in the life of the individuals have not created some of the observed differences in performance. There may well be some significant average differences between populations in respect to metabolism and temperature regulation. Further studies of these are urgently needed; we are just beginning to see reports of experiments that carefully control non-racial factors that might masquerade as racial differences (Baker, 1960). It is logical to believe, for example, that, whatever their origin, peoples whose ancestors have long lived in the tropics may come to differ in heat tolerance from those whose ancestral home is the Arctic. But these differences will probably prove to be small, for man in the Arctic always has clothing, shelter, and fire and need not rely on purely physiological mechanisms of cold adaptation.

GENERAL REFERENCES

Hooton, E. A., 1946, *Up from the Ape,* 2d ed. New York: The Macmillan Company. Pages 568–661 give a picture of world racial distributions that is as authoritative and as satisfactory as any static view can be.

UNESCO, 1952, *The Race Concept.* Paris: UNESCO, and New York: Columbia University Press. The UNESCO statement on race is a consensus of scientific opinion concerning race and capacity and is followed by a full statement of the few differing opinions.

18 · Measurement of Man

Anthropometry

In the halls of the medical school where I teach I frequently meet a professor of neurosurgery. His invariable greeting is: "Have you measured any skulls today?" My answer is usually negative. So far in this book we have barely mentioned skull sizes. Today much anthropological research is concerned with geology, genetics, and demography, with never a thought of putting calipers to skulls. But this has not always been the case. The first writings on physical anthropology consisted of descriptions of distant peoples or speculations on their origin. Such studies, however, soon gave way to the measurement of men. Somewhat over a century ago a famous German anatomist-anthropologist, Rudolf Virchow, attempted to get his scientific colleagues to standardize some ways of measuring the skull. At about the same time in France another anatomist-anthropologist, Paul Broca, set himself a similar task. From that time to the present, physical anthropologists have studied the human body and especially its bony parts as geometrical shapes. Such shapes can be described and compared in terms of dimensions, angles, and proportions.

This technique, known as anthropometry, has greatly enhanced our appreciation of the subtlety of human differences and the variety of human forms. A hundred years ago, Dr. Anders Retzius (1860), a Swedish anatomist-anthropologist, demonstrated that the ratio of maximum length to maximum breadth of the skull varies from place to place and that the *cephalic index, as he called it, can be* used as a basis for racial classification. Retzius also considered the

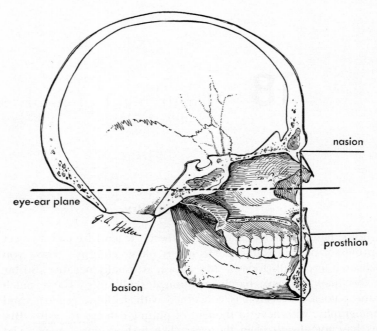

Fig. 18-1. A median section of a human skull, showing cranial landmarks: nasion, prosthion, and basion. The extent to which prosthion is anterior to a vertical line through nasion at right angles to the eye-ear plane is a measure of prognathism.

degree of prognathism in his racial classification. Various landmarks on the skull can be used for measurements. The prominent point between the brows (glabella) and the point farthest back on the skull (opisthion) define head length. Three other points in the midline define the facial triangle and indicate prognathism. They are *nasion,* the juncture of the nasal and frontal bones; *prosthion,* the point of bone between the upper central incisor teeth; and *basion,* the anterior margin of the foramen magnum (Fig. 18-1). Some of these points are readily identified, and such measurements as cephalic index and face height (the nasion-prosthion distance) can be determined, on living individuals as well as on ancient skulls. Other points such as basion can be seen only on the skull (or a carefully posed x-ray), and measures of head height and prognathism (the degree to which prosthion lies in front of a vertical line through nasion) tend to be inexact on the living.

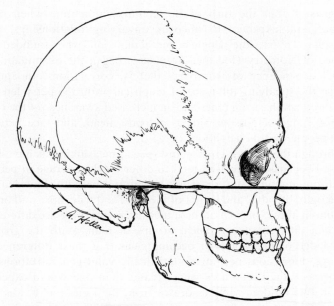

Fig. 18-2. The eye-ear plane through the top of both ear holes and lower margin of the orbits. In conjunction with a median plane bisecting the skull and a plane at right angles to both of these through the ear holes, the eye-ear plane is the basis for a descriptive cranial geometry.

In 1879, a convention at Frankfurt, Germany, of anatomists interested in anthropology agreed upon a standard position for holding the skull. The so-called "Frankfurt horizontal" or "eye-ear plane" (Fig. 18-2) consists of a plane through the top of both ear holes and the lowest point on the lower margin of the orbits. By adding a vertical plane that bisects the skull (the median or midsagittal plane) and a third plane at right angles to both of these, through the ear holes, any point on the skull can be located by its rectilinear distances from these three planes. If enough measurements are made by means of these coordinates, one person can describe a skull accurately enough for someone else to draw it.

Anthropology and Statistics

Many of the techniques of statistical analysis of probabilities, now applied in every field of science, were first developed by anthropologists. About the turn of the century, at a time when other sciences still expected to uncover unvarying relationships, Karl Pearson (1896), the English mathematician who founded the science of biometry (life measurement), began the examination of partial dependence of variables—that is, correlations. In anthropology the steadying influence of empirical anthropometry led to a decreased emphasis on types and an increased awareness of the overlapping range of possible shapes of body, head, and face between each people and its neighbors.

Through the years a great many special measurements have been devised because dimensions tend to differ on the average in peoples of various regions. Stature, trunk height and breadth, limb lengths, and length, breadth, and height of the head and face, nose and orbits, are among these. In each of these measurements there are differences between different geographical groups of man. With the growing knowledge of probability it became clear that these differences in average dimensions permitted statistically valid generalizations: In many cases the differences were greater than one would expect to find in two random samples drawn from the same lot. It was generally assumed, therefore, that these "real" differences (technically called *significant* by the statistician) were racial—that is, they provided evidence of different genetic origins—although statistical tests were not applied to this assumption. This line of argument perhaps reached its culmination in Coon's (1939) book, *The Races of Europe*. Considering the limitations and complexity of the material, he succeeded as well as anyone could in untangling the racial picture of so hybrid a continental population. The technique of adding measurement to measurement was designed to increase the precision of the description. Such descriptions of peoples became quite precise, but long before Coon published his work, anthropologists had begun to wonder whether the characteristics described were entirely hereditary in origin and how much they could tell us about race.

Migration and Environment

Early in the present century some anthropologists first asked whether the traits that were being used to characterize races could be influenced directly by environmental factors. They did not mean

Lamarck's theory of inheritance of acquired characteristics, which had already been discredited; nor did they mean Darwin's description of the selectivity of the natural environment. The question was: Would people grow up to be physically different if they lived differently? In 1905, Dr. G. Walcher, a German obstetrician, showed that when babies are regularly placed on the backs of their heads they become broader headed than do babies who are customarily placed on their sides. In the same year, a New Yorker, Maurice Fishberg, compared measurements of the cephalic index and stature of Jews in various parts of Europe and in the United States and found that the two groups differed in these respects from each other. If cephalic index and stature could change in immigrants of at least one European group, how could these measurements be used as major criteria of race?

At this time many Americans were concerned with the assimilation of immigrants. Franz Boas, usually considered the father of American anthropology, exploited this concern in getting support from the United States Immigration Commission for a survey of the physical measurements of immigrants. Whatever may have been the expectations of the Commission, Boas characteristically set himself a concrete problem and defined it operationally. Are the American-born children of European immigrants significantly different from their parents in such characteristics as cephalic index and stature? If so, do they also differ in the same respects from their immigrant brothers and sisters? Boas completed his survey and published the chief results in 1910. Of the various groups Boas studied, his largest samples were of Central European Jews, and Italians from Sicily. In both groups the American-born offspring tended to be taller than their parents; but in the Jews the cephalic index decreased, in the Sicilians it increased. The measurements of the immigrant brothers and sisters, correlation with the length of the time the parents had been in the United States, and smaller studies of other nationalities led to the conclusion that the changes were the result of some aspect of the American environment that tends to bring about an American type of tall stature and medium cephalic index.

Some anthropologists who had used similar measurements in an attempt to untangle racial history firmly believed that these measurements reflect inheritance. They attempted to explain Boas' findings on the basis of some selection, perhaps a self-selection of immigrants.

In order to examine the possibility of such selection of immigrants, as well as the possibility of changes in the offspring of immigrants, H. L. Shapiro, the curator of anthropology at the American Museum of Natural History in New York, in collaboration with F. Hulse and W. A. Lessa, both graduate students at the time, undertook studies of two national groups in Hawaii, the Chinese and Japanese. Besides migrants and Hawaiian-born persons, his study included the stay-at-homes in the Orient, for whom Shapiro coined the word "sedentes." Of the Chinese study only a brief preliminary report ever appeared (Shapiro, 1931). The Japanese study, however, has been fully presented. Shapiro (1939) found that the Hawaiian-born Japanese were taller and broader headed, and that they differed significantly from Japanese immigrants in this and numerous other respects. He also reported, however, that the immigrants were different from the sedentes in many dimensions—including many in which the Hawaiian-born differed from the immigrants. Shapiro explained the difference between sedentes and migrants on the basis of selection, and that between migrants and Hawaiian-born persons on the basis of factors in the environment during the growth period. The general findings of Boas and Shapiro have been confirmed by a number of small studies, including one of my own on Chinese in continental United States (Lasker, 1946).

Nevertheless, a number of problems remained. In the various studies the immigrants measured were older than the American-born, and to some extent this fact might explain the differences. There is a tendency for individuals to decrease somewhat in height after the age of 30 or so, and, in addition, people are getting taller from generation to generation all over the world; both in Japan and the United States, for example, adult sons are taller than their fathers (and also taller than their fathers were at the same age). Such increases have been going on for 100 years and possibly for 200 or more years. Gordon Bowles (1932), a Japanese-born American anthropologist, has shown that Harvard sons of Harvard fathers are taller than their fathers were at the same age. The sons are larger in most other bodily measurements also; markedly so in the length of their thighs and forearms.

To take account of local trends as well as the effects of migration, Marcus S. Goldstein (1943), a student of Boas, undertook a study in Mexico of Mexican parents and their adult children and a parallel study of Mexican immigrants to the United States and their adult American-born children. He found that the immigrants were larger in the usual respects than the sedentes, that the younger adults in Mexico were larger than their like-sexed parents, and that those born in the United States were larger than their parents. The last difference was the most pronounced, however, and seemed to indicate a growth factor that is especially strong in the United States.

These findings are in general confirmed by a series of studies of my own (Lasker, 1952, 1954B) and my former colleague in the Department of Anatomy at Wayne State University, Dr. F. Gaynor Evans.

What is there in the environment of the United States that accounts for the changed pattern of growth? Despite the fact that the pattern of physical changes is fairly constant in studies of migrants, such studies do not isolate specific causes. In taking the circumstances of the studies into consideration, I am inclined to minimize the probable significance of variations in climate, altitude, and hygiene. It seems likely to me that the biggest single factor is diet, and that the most significant aspect of diet is not the quality or the vitamin content, but simply the quantity, of food. Of social conditions, economic status would therefore be the most important. This is only a hypothesis, however, and its confirmation or disproof will require careful growth experiments, probably on animals closely related to man, such as monkeys.

Heredity Versus Environment in Twins

Another possible way to discover the relative importance of genetic and environmental factors is in the growth of twins. Twins are of two types: *monozygous* (one-egged)—or identical—twins, formed from a single fertilized ovum and having identical genes; and *dizygous* (two-egged), formed from two ova, separately fertilized. Dizygous twins are genetically no more closely related to each other than ordinary brothers and sisters and are therefore sometimes referred to as fraternal twins. In 1937, Professor H. H. Newman of the University of Chicago and his associates published a study of 119 pairs of twins. As one might expect, the so-called identical twins were much more similar to each other in physique than were the fraternal pairs. The most interesting finding, however, pertained to 19 pairs of monozygous twins who had been separated shortly after birth and reared apart in different social and physical environments. These pairs showed greater differences than the monozygous twins reared together in respect to weight and especially in respect to scores on intelligence tests, but not appreciably in respect to eye color and pattern or size and shape of ears, nose, head, and face. A larger number of significant differences might conceivably have been noted had more twins been studied, had the contrast in their environments been greater, or had more measurements been made.

Plasticity, a Factor Minimizing Selection

The significance for human evolution of *plasticity*—the capacity of the individual to change in response to his environment—is not what Lamarck and many others have assumed it to be. Lamarck believed that acquired characteristics would be inherited by the offspring. Beginning in 1883 experimental geneticists attempted without success to adduce evidence for the inheritance of acquired characteristics. They therefore concluded that all inherited characteristics are transmitted in the germ plasm. This theory has been somewhat modified as we have come to know more about the variety of genetic mechanisms. Nevertheless, it is safe to say that, to the extent that pre-emigrants are not a select group physically when compared with other sedentes, there is no reason to expect their offspring to differ genetically from those of the sedentes. We have therefore ascribed the differences actually found, as in Goldstein's study, to environmental influences on growth.

Suppose, however, the migrants are selected for greater size and more robust physique. Small and weak men may less often attempt to emigrate or may be turned back by the border officials. In the case of the Mexican contract laborers, the representatives of the United States Department of Agriculture examined their hands, and I did find that the migrants had wider hands than the nonmigrants.

The factors making for larger size and greater robustness are presumably both hereditary and environmental. To the extent that these factors are hereditary, the children will also be large and strong, but to the extent that they are environmental, the children will, if they live in the sedente environment, tend to revert to the average of the sedentes. In 1942, Paul Ito found that American-born Japanese women who had lived in Japan were intermediate in body measurements between those who had lived only in America and those who had lived only in Japan. In other words, the greater the relative significance of the environmental growth factors, the less the effect of selective migration on the genetic differentiation of migrants. The selection of phenotypes for a particular characteristic will be crude and ineffective if the characteristic is highly plastic. Plasticity is thus adaptively advantageous and a conservative factor in evolution. Children who have plenty to eat throughout childhood may grow into larger adults. Larger adults require more food to survive. If a subsequent period of food deprivation were to stunt the growth of the next generation, however, they would grow into smaller individuals, capable—other things being equal—of maintaining their weight on fewer calories per day. Markowitz (1955), while an undergraduate at the University of Wisconsin, published a critique of growth studies that had been made in a dozen countries of Asia and Europe during World War II; all of these demonstrate a definite tendency to stunting, a reversal of the constant prewar increases in size.

Man has evolved a large number of capacities that spare him the necessity of evolving special modifications for each environment. Most of these capacities are shared with other animals and must be the ancient product of our mammalian forebears. Man can maintain a body temperature of approximately 98.6° Fahrenheit despite considerable variation in the external climate. Similarly, he can produce antibodies to all sorts of diseases when he is exposed to them and thus does not need to inherit antibodies preformed to combat each of thousands of infectious organisms.

Modifications for life at high altitudes are especially noteworthy. At an altitude of 8000 feet the air is considerably thinner, and one needs to increase the capacity for oxygenation of blood by some 25 percent to nourish the tissues of the body. At higher altitudes the demands on the body are progressively greater. Acclimatization may be achieved by: reduced activity (thereby reducing the body tissues' need for oxygenated blood), increased rate of breathing, or increased capacity of the blood to transport oxygen. Mountain climbers at high altitudes experience all these functional changes: They slow down, their breathing quickens, and the number of red blood cells (erythrocytes) in their blood greatly increases. All these changes are reversed when the climber returns to lower altitudes. In my studies at about 8000 feet altitude in Mexico I found no significant difference in chest dimensions among those who had spent their whole life at that altitude and those who had spent much of it elsewhere. At much higher elevations in the Andes, however, a Peruvian physician, Dr. Carlos Monge (1953) has found that the people have significantly larger chests. He believes that the mountain peoples inherit a number of such characteristics which fit them for mountain life, and he calls the people he studied the "Andean race." Monge has stated that it is quite possible the characteristic features of this "race" would not develop fully in offspring of members who spent all their lives in the low country. However, I have measured Peruvian fishermen of Indian extraction whose ancestors for many generations have lived on the coast, and they have the large deep chests and broad shoulders of the Andean race. Nevertheless, plasticity as well as race may well be involved in the highland Andean type. Man's physical capacity to meet the situation is great. A New Zealander of English descent and a high-plateau Tibetan Sherpa made the first successful ascent of Mount Everest; Matthew Henson, an American Negro, accompanied Admiral Peary on all his arctic explorations, and Henson, Peary, and four Eskimos were the first men to reach the North Pole.

Plasticity, as I have used the term, refers to capacity to change within the lifetime of the individual. It applies especially to those permanent effects that may occur as a result of changed environment during the growth period. As we have seen, the greater the adaptive plasticity the less the necessity for adaptive natural selection. Because of this great difference in the mechanisms, it might be well to avoid the term "adaptive" used in the specific way that paleontologists do, or to couple it with the word "fitness" (which suggests Darwin's own phrase, "survival of the fittest") when referring to adaptation through selective survival of persons with specific genes or constellations of genes.

Within this frame of reference, then, there are really two quite different modes of adaptation: In the one, natural selection operates in the particular local situation to adapt all successive generations to the current conditions; in the other, any member of the species can directly adapt to new environments without any genetic modification. Of course, this plasticity itself has presumably been selected.

GENERAL REFERENCE

Kaplan, Bernice A., 1954, "Environment and Human Plasticity," *American Anthropologist,* 56: 780–800. A review of migration studies.

19 · Growth Patterns in the Individual

The Measurement of Growth

As noted earlier, the techniques of anthropometry were developed at a time when it was believed that they could be used to solve the problems of race. While this hope has waned, new uses of the techniques have emerged. When anthropologists wished to compare the measurements of two groups of adults, the question soon arose: At what age do people reach their adult dimensions? The solution was sought by arranging the statures by age groups and seeing at what age increases in stature ceased. It was noted that this age occurred later in men than in women (it is still a common practice arbitrarily to consider as adults women over 16 years of age and men over 18). The anthropologist was now fully engaged in study of the question of physiological adolescence and the study of the growth process. When statures of individuals are arranged by age, it is seen that there are certain periods of very rapid growth and certain periods of slower progress. The first spurt normally follows the first week of life and continues at a gradually decreased rate for the first four years or so. Growth then continues at a slower pace but starts to go ahead faster again in the period before puberty. During the interval, girls, who on the average are smaller at birth than boys, briefly exceed the boys in average height. In various groups which have been studied, this period usually occurs from the age of about 9 to about 12. The growth curve of the girls decelerates after puberty, and their stature reaches stability several years later, while boys reach puberty later and continue to grow at least into their twenties.

Longitudinal Growth Studies

The above description is very general. There are considerable differences that depend on race and environment, and, furthermore, there are marked individual differences. Growth curves based on groups of different ages, such as all the children of a certain school, show considerable fluctuations and, if the time intervals are short, even occasionally an apparent downward trend. These fluctuations are recognized as biologically meaningless and merely the result of the limited size of the samples studied. They occur when measurements of one set of individuals at one age are compared with those of another set of individuals at a different age.

The first recorded instance of a systematic attempt to follow the growth of an individual was undertaken between April 11, 1759, and January 30, 1777 (Scammon, 1927). During this period, Philibert Gueneau de Montbeillard, a French country gentleman, measured his son's height twice a year. On the basis of these data his friend, the celebrated French naturalist Georges Louis Leclerc de Buffon, noted that growth is greater in summer than in winter. Buffon also was the first to state that stature tends to decrease during the day and increase after a night's rest.

Information of this kind and also conclusions concerning individual differences in the growth process can be derived only from remeasuring the same individuals. Such a growth study is called longitudinal (Fig. 19-1), while surveys employing only one examination of each individual are called cross-sectional.

One conclusion from longitudinal studies is that the pubescent growth spurt is much sharper than appears from cross-sectional data, but that variations in the age at which it occurs make it appear more gradual when data from different individuals are averaged. This suggests that chronological age may not be the best way of measuring growth progress. In girls the pubescent growth changes are more closely related to the time of the first menses (called menarche) than they are to age. Such secondary sexual character-

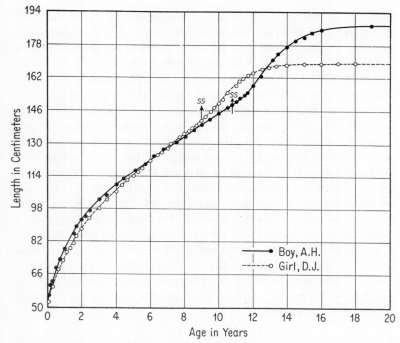

Fig. 19-1. Growth charts of body length measurements in an individual boy and girl. The beginning of the prepubertal spurts in growth are marked (SS). (From *Human Biology, 29,* 1957. Courtesy of Jean Deming.)

istics as development of body hair, breasts, and in boys the change of voice are also in better sequence with the growth pattern than is mere age. T. Wingate Todd, professor of anatomy at Western Reserve University, noted that the ages at which various bones ossify and the parts of a bone fuse with each other also are closely related to the growth process, and he introduced the concept of "physiological age" as a measure of growth progress. Predictions of adult stature based on the degree of ossification achieved are more reliable than those based on achieved age.

Growth and Health

Endocrinal, nutritional, and other diseases of childhood usually affect the rate of growth; hence, individual progress in growth in weight or in the ratio of stature to weight serves as an index of health. Several different schemes have been devised whereby a physician or teacher can look for abberations in the growth pattern that may reflect ill health. One of these methods is that of Dr. N. C. Wetzel, a Cleveland pediatrician, who has produced a graph on which weight is plotted on the vertical axis and height on the horizontal. As a child grows in both dimensions the plotted dots angle up toward the right. The graph has a series of diagonal lines drawn toward the upper right, and the spaces between these lines Wetzel calls channels. The scales are so designed that a normal healthy child will tend to stay in the same channel. Deviations from channel-wise growth or lack of a normal amount of growth within the channel are suggestive of ill health. Other types of chart serve the same purpose. All suffer, however, from the difficulty that healthy growth varies from race to race and person to person, and that "normal" is impossible to define satisfactorily. Most anthropologists define normal in statistical terms—that is, "like most other children." Wetzel is less specific about how he uses anthropometric data in establishing his norms: To him they are intended to have clinical as well as statistical meaning.

Differential Growth

The type of chart mentioned in the previous section can ultimately give no information except about height and weight. These are compound measurements that encompass many factors and are therefore excellent measures of general size. Any analysis of what makes up size requires some measurement of the segments, however. Once this need was recognized, anthropologists were ready with techniques for measuring just such body segments. It was soon apparent that different segments of the body grow at different rates at different times. For example, by the time of birth, the human head has come to dominate the little body, but during the postnatal period the body and then the limbs tend to spurt ahead to produce adult proportions. Growth is thus asymmetrical in a way analogous to the asymmetry of evolution. In human development the head grows rapidly, then the limbs and trunk, and the ears and nose continue to grow throughout life; in human evolution, the hind limbs apparently evolved rapidly before the main expansion of the brain and skull, and some changes in details of the external nose and ears are probably recent. Although there is no simple alternation of "spring up" and "spread out" during growth, as was once believed, various lengths and breadths grow fastest at different times.

Like many biological phenomena, the relative growth of two parts or of two dimensions is often such that the ratio of the logarithms of the measurements remains constant for considerable periods of time. This kind of relationship is called *allometry*. It is particularly helpful because it calls attention to critical phases in growth—the times at which the logarithmic ratios change.

The tissues of the body as well as the segments show different growth patterns. Lymphatic tissue and the thymus gland develop early in childhood and actually regress considerably in adulthood. The brain and other nervous tissues also develop early, and their growth rapidly decelerates in early childhood. The gonads (ovaries and testes), on the other hand, and the secondary sexual tissues such as breasts develop very little at first but suddenly spurt ahead at puberty. Most other body tissues show an intermediate type of growth that reflects general growth: They show the infantile and pubescent spurts and more moderate growth rates between these times. A growth curve of muscle or bone is similar to one of stature or weight.

Body Fat

Growth in fat has come to have special interest because actuarial statisticians working for life insurance companies have adduced evidence that fat persons, especially fat men, have a shorter expectation of life than average or lean persons. Fat people seem especially subject to certain heart and kidney ailments. Only recently, anthropologists have begun to test and use a variety of methods of measuring body fat: Subcutaneous fat can be determined by picking up a double fold of skin and underlying tissue and applying calipers with a spring that exerts a known pressure; subcutaneous fat can also be measured on x-rays; total body fat can be estimated from specific gravity, which is determined by dunking the person and weighing him under water—the method for measuring his body volume that Archimedes discovered during his famous bath.

Total body fat can be roughly measured by body weight or by some index using height and weight. So measured, the amount of fat has long been known to depend on the amount of food eaten. The exact distribution patterns of body fat are only now becoming known, however. In some racial groups such as the Hottentot there seems to be a special proclivity for fat to deposit on the buttocks (called steatopygea) and on the thighs. There are also characteristic differences, on the average, between male and female fat distribution patterns. In American men, at least, total body fat appears to increase with age, even in persons who do not gain in weight, at least into the fifties. The genetics of fat patterns and the relation of fatness to disease are problems now being actively studied by anthropologists in collaboration with biochemists and physicians. The National Research Council recently convened a conference that considered the use of body measurements in evaluating human nutrition. The conference recommended a standard list of measurements to be used in nutritional surveys (Brožek, 1956).

Facial Growth and Orthodontics

Numerous other application of precise body measurements to the healing arts have called on the skill of anthropometry. One of these, measurement of facial growth in relation to shape of jaws and position of teeth, has called for collaborative efforts of anthropologists and orthodontists (dentists specializing in straightening the teeth). Especially among Europeans and peoples of European culture, wherever they live and whatever their race, there is a large proportion whose teeth seem too big for their jaws or whose jaws seem unmatched to each other. While some consider these disharmonies inherent, others have demonstrated situations in which dietary and other habits are largely responsible. The teeth may be rotated or crowded out of the tooth row, and upper teeth may fail to meet the lower ones or may do so in an unsatisfactory manner. Such malocclusions interfere with adequate chewing and are considered ugly. To correct these malformations, orthodontists move the teeth in the jaw by the application of mechanical forces. Unless the orthodontist can predict the amount of future growth of the jaws of children, the process may not be effective or may produce other maladjustments.

To obtain adequately accurate measurements of growth potential, anthropologists and radiologists have devised a number of techniques to x-ray the head under standardized conditions that permit the restudy of the same individual later. These techniques of *cephalometry* consist of taking a true lateral view, by inserting plugs in the ear holes and aligning the two plugs with the central beam of the x-ray. The junction of the nasal bones with the frontal bone (nasion) and other bony landmarks can be identified on the x-ray films, and changes in dimensions and angles can be determined with millimeter accuracy (more precise than most caliper measurements of actual bones). A controversy has arisen concerning the best "central point" of the head from which to measure growth in the various directions; any choice, however, is an arbitrary one. We know this from experimental studies in which animals are injected with a dye (such as alizarin red S) that stains growing bone but not already formed bone (Baer, 1954, for example). These studies demonstrate that each cranial bone grows more or less independently at its various edges and, in some cases, surfaces (Mednick and Washburn, 1956). The way to take the measurements for orthodontic purposes can best be determined by the practical test of usefulness in treating patients. For the basic studies of the anthropologist, the best units of study of growth in man may be suggested by the natural units of growth observed in experimental animals stained with alizarin.

GENERAL REFERENCES

Reynolds, Earle L., 1952, "The Distribution of Subcutaneous Fat in Childhood and Adolescence," *Monographs of the Society for Research in Child Development,* Vol. 15, Serial No. 50, No. 2, 1950. The report of a long-time study of body fat.

Tanner, J. M., 1955, *Growth at Adolescence,* Springfield, Ill.: C. C. Thomas. A survey rather than a summary of studies of the maturational phase of growth.

Zuckerman, Solly, ed., 1950, "A Discussion on the Measurement of Growth and Form," *Proceedings, Royal Society of London,* Series B, No. 137. See especially the article by C. H. Waddington on the biological measurement of growth and form.

20 · Evolution and the Future

The story of man's changing place in nature has led us into several scientific asides. Nevertheless it has brought a partial answer to the question of the origin of the species. We have seen the changing forms of human ancestors and their collateral kinsmen achieving the traits that make us human. More significant still, we have learned much about the nature of human evolution—the genetic processes by which such endowments have been transmitted and altered in the past and may be transmitted and altered in the future. We thus have a frame into which we can fit the picture manifest by fossils still to be unearthed.

In establishing this framework we have examined the question of race. Racial characteristics, it is clear, are any hereditary characteristics that vary from one group of people with common ancestry, to another. Some such traits may be particularly advantageous for life under certain conditions, although this is usually difficult to establish, and some racial differences are more plausibly explained as the result of historical coincidence. In any case, traits advantageous to members of a particular race today are the property of the whole human species tomorrow. There is enough interbreeding, at least between neighboring groups, for genetic endowments eventually to spread to all peoples who follow a way of life in which the traits would confer advantages for survival. Genetic diversity of mankind is clearly an asset for our descendants. Those who inherit our good points, and in whom someone else's good points are substituted for our bad, may naturally be chosen.

Eugenics is the subject that has to do with factors that improve hereditary qualities; the question of the deliberate choice of mates, or the decision whether to reproduce or not, are part of its concern. Partially because of public reaction to overenthusiastic and sometimes erroneous claims of its adherents, eugenics so far has had little effect in eliminating hereditary diseases or otherwise modifying future generations. But eugenics also may become an important force as a sense of responsibility for the future becomes a stronger element of social ethics, and as the knowledge on which scientifically informed choices can be made becomes more general. Today the effects of planned parenthood in such countries as the United States seem to be to bring the number of offspring of families close to a generally accepted idea of a normal family (one with three or four children). Furthermore, although some parents of offspring with hereditary (usually recessive) defects show reproductive restraint, others tend to compensate for births of defective children by deciding to have further children. For the future, regardless of the legal restraints in one or another country, it seems likely that artificial insemination—with the possibility of a single father for scores of children—will be practiced in some places. Moreover, with techniques now under development, semen can be preserved so that men long dead may sire children. This may lead to close inbreeding. In the future, also, man may be able to affect the likelihood of having male or female offspring, since sperm determining the two sexes differ, albeit little. The various prospects of such events can be estimated in advance and studied in process by human geneticists; we already have the capacity to identify an imminent danger to the species before it is swamped by a load of disadvantageous genes.

There is no assurance of human "progress," however. The impact of human agency, which can release toxic substances and radiation into the air we breathe and the food we eat, may outstrip natural or deliberate selection. Natural history, too, imposes new conditions: changes in the animals, plants, things, and climate that surround us. And man is changing his relationship to his environment. The world is rapidly becoming one in which the immediate surroundings and resources are losing the direct influence they have had on human evolution through the selective process man shares with the animal world. Not only is more of the environment man made, but the local environment becomes almost inconsequential for continued human evolution as mobility constantly increases and as the larger terrestrial environment makes new demands on body and mind, necessitating a high degree of plasticity in responding to different natural and artificially produced conditions. Eventually possibilities of space travel may add yet another dimension to the environment in which man must be able to function in order to survive, or at least leave his offspring equipped with the essential capacities for effective mastery of the total environment.

This account of human evolution has covered great spans of time past through an analysis of the fossil "pithecuses" and "anthropuses." Emphasis has also been given to ongoing evolution in man. But whether through the long-term changes seen in the fossil record or through the short-term changes of population genetics, the key to understanding evolution in the future lies in an analysis of the processes involved. And, as Garrett Hardin (1959), professor of biology at the University of California at Goleta, says in *Nature and Man's Fate:*

> It doesn't much matter whether you think man was created out of dust six thousand years ago or came from apes a million years earlier. . . . Believe what you will of evolution in the past: but you had jolly well better believe it will take place in the future if you hope to make political decisions that will give your descendants a reasonable chance to exist.

Furthermore, in such a time as ours, progress along the established lines, however great it has been in the recent past, cannot be held to meet the need for new knowledge. There is needed also a new vigor in approach to both old and new problems. The best evidence that physical anthropology possesses this vigor lies in the uncompromising directness with which so many of its practitioners are attacking complex problems. Without abandoning the rigor of proven methods, or the painful accumulation of detailed additions to knowledge that has been so fruitful in the past, they are willing to reexamine concepts that may no longer suffice to explain the multitude of collected data, and to explore new hypotheses—sometimes suggested by an excursion into the realm of an allied scientific discipline—that would account for a wider range of facts. They are creating a theoretical basis of physical anthropology in closer harmony with the now rapidly changing conceptual structure of the universe and of man's place in it.

In physical anthropology there are branches where, as has been shown, general theory and methodology are sufficiently far advanced to permit of considerable specialization, both in further research and in application to specific problems. The greatest need and the greatest opportunity for the development of the science is to be found, however, in the search for comprehensive understandings: of the origin of man, of the functioning of his body as a whole, of its responses to the environment, and of its evolutionary potential.

GENERAL REFERENCE

Hardin, Garrett, 1959, *Nature and Man's Fate*. New York: Holt, Rinehart and Winston, Inc. An explanation of evolution and its meaning for man.

Literature Cited

Akeley, Carl E., 1923, "Gorillas—real and mythical," *Natural History,* Journal of the American Museum of Natural History, New York, 23: 428–447.

Allison, A. C., 1954, "Protection afforded by sickle-cell trait against subtertian malarial infection," *British Medical Journal,* 1: 290–294.

Angel, J. Lawrence, 1951, "The human skeletal remains from Hotu Cave, Iran," *Proceedings of the American Philosophical Society,* 96: 258–269.

Anonymous, 1957, "Archeological discoveries in Iraq," *Science,* 126: 834–835.

Arambourg, C., 1955, "A recent discovery in human paleontology: Atlanthropus of Ternifine (Algeria)," *American Journal of Physical Anthropology,* 13: 191–201. 1956 "Une troisième mandibule d'Atlanthropus découverte à Ternifine (Algeria)," *Quaternaria,* new series, Vol. 3.

———, and P. Biberson, 1956, "The fossil human remains from the palaeolithic site of Sidi Abderrahman (Morocco)," *American Journal of Physical Anthropology,* new series, 14: 467–489.

Ashton, E. H., and Solly Zuckerman, 1951, "The influence of geographic isolation on the skull of the green monkey (*Cercopithecus aethiops sabaeus*)," III and IV, *Proceedings of the Royal Society of London,* series B, 138: 354–374.

Baer, Melvyn J., 1954, "Patterns of growth of the skull as revealed by vital staining," *Human Biology,* 26: 80–126.

Baker, Paul T., 1960, "Climate, culture and evolution," *Human Biology,* 32: 3–16.

Bernstein, Felix, 1924, "Ergebnisse einer biostatistischen zusammenfassenden Betrachtung über die erblichen Blutstrukturen des Menschen," *Klinische Wochenschrift,* 3: 1495–1497.

Beutler, Ernest, 1959, "The hemolitic effect of primaquine and related compounds: a review," *Blood*, 14:103–139.

Birdsell, Joseph B., 1948, "The racial origin of the extinct Tasmanians," Records of the Queen Victoria Museum, 2(3). 1950, reprinted in *Yearbook of Physical Anthropology—1950*, pp. 143–160.

———, 1951, "Some implications of the genetical concept of race in terms of spatial analysis," *Cold Spring Harbor Symposia on Quantitative Biology*, 15: 259–314.

———, 1957, "Some population problems involving Pleistocene man," *Cold Spring Harbor Symposia on Quantitative Biology*, 22: 47–69.

Black, Davidson, 1927, "On a lower molar hominid tooth from the Choukoutien deposit," *Palaeontologia Sinica*, series D, 7:1–28.

Boas, Franz, 1910, "Changes in bodily form of descendants of immigrants," Senate Document 208, 61st Congress, 2d Session, Washington, D.C.

Bowles, Gordon, 1932, *New types of old Americans at Harvard*. Cambridge, Mass.: Harvard University Press.

Boyd, William C., 1950, *Genetics and the races of man, an introduction to modern physical anthropology*. Boston: Little, Brown and Company.

Broom, Robert, 1949, "The ape-man," *Scientific American*, 181: 20–24. Reprinted in *Yearbook of Physical Anthropology—1949*, pp. 65–69.

Brožek, Josef, ed., 1956, *Body measurements and human nutrition*. Detroit: Wayne University Press. Reprinted from *Human Biology*, 28: 109–273 (1956).

Brues, Alice, 1954, "Selection and polymorphism in the A-B-O blood groups," *American Journal of Physical Anthropology*, new series, 12: 559–597.

Calvin, Melvin, 1956, "Chemical evolution and the origin of life," *American Scientist*, 44: 248–263.

Carcassi, U., R. Ceppellini, and F. Pitzus, 1957, "Frequenza della talassemia in quattro popolazione sarde e suoi rapporti con la distribuzione dei gruppi sanguigni e della malaria," *Bollettino dell' Istituto Sieroterapico Milanese*, 36: 206–218.

Carpenter, Charles R., 1934, "A field study of the behavior and social relations of howling monkeys (*Alouatta palliata*)," *Comparative Psychology Monographs*, Vol. 10, serial no. 48. Baltimore: The Johns Hopkins Press.

———, 1935, "Behavior of red spider monkeys in Panama," *Journal of Mammalogy*, 16:171–180.

———, 1940, "A field study in Siam of the behavior and social rela-

tions of the gibbon (*Hylobates lar*)," *Comparative Psychology Monographs*, Vol. 16, No. 5. Baltimore: The Johns Hopkins Press.
————, 1942, "Sexual behavior of free ranging rhesus monkeys (*Macaca mulatta*)." I, "Specimens, procedures and behavioral characteristics of estrus"; II, "Periodicity of estrus, homosexual, autoerotic and non-conformist behavior," *Journal of Comparative Psychology*, 33: 113–162.

Clark, W. E. Le Gros, 1955, *The fossil evidence for human evolution*. Chicago: University of Chicago Press.

Collias, Nicholas, and Charles Southwick, 1952, "A field study of population density and social organization in howling monkeys," *Proceedings of the American Philosophical Society*, 96: 143–156.

Cooley, Thomas B., and Pearl Lee, 1925, "A series of cases of splenomegaly in children, with anemia and peculiar bone changes," *Transactions of the American Pediatric Society*, 37th Session, pp. 29–30.

Coon, Carleton Stevens, 1939, *The races of Europe*. New York: Macmillan.
————, 1960, "Race and ecology in man," *Cold Spring Harbor Symposia on Quantitative Biology*, 24: 153–159.
————, S. M. Garn, and J. B. Birdsell, 1950, *Races: A study of the problems of race formation in man*. Springfield, Ill.: C. C. Thomas.

Dart, Raymond A., 1925, "*Australopithecus africanus:* The man-ape of South Africa," *Nature*, 115: 195–199.

Darwin, Charles, 1871, *Descent of man and selection in relation to sex*, 2d ed. revised and augmented. New York: Appleton, 1909.

DeTerra, Helmut, 1956, "New approach to the problem of man's origin," *Science*, 124: 1282–1285.

Dobzhansky, Th., 1951, *Genetics and the origin of species*, 3d ed., revised. New York: Columbia University Press.

Dollo, Louis, 1893, "Les Lois de l'Évolution," *Bulletin de Société Belge de Geologie*, 7: 164–166.

Drennan, M. R., 1956, "Note on the morphological status of the Swanscombe and Fontéchevade skulls," *American Journal of Physical Anthropology*, new series, 14: 73–83.

Dreyer, T. F., 1947, "Further observations on the Florisbad skull," *Soölogiese Navorsing van die Nasionale Museum*, 1: 183–190. Reprinted (with corrections) in *Yearbook of Physical Anthropology—1947*, pp. 271–278.

DuChaillu, Paul B., 1861, *Explorations and adventures in Equatorial Africa*. London.

Eaton, Joseph W., and Albert J. Mayer, 1953, "The social biology of very high fertility among the Hutterites. The demography of a unique population," *Human Biology,* 25: 206–264.

Emiliani, Cesare, 1956, "Note on absolute chronology of human evolution," *Science,* 123: 924–926.

Fishberg, Maurice, 1905, "Materials for the physical anthropology of the eastern European Jew," *Annals of the New York Academy of Science,* 16: 155–297.

Fisher, R. A., 1930, *The genetical theory of natural selection.* Oxford.

Garn, S. M., and C. S. Coon, 1955, "On the number of races of mankind," *American Anthropologist,* 57: 996–1001.

———, and A. B. Lewis, 1958, "Tooth size, body size and 'giant' fossil man," *American Anthropologist,* 60: 874–880.

Garrod, Archibald E., 1902, "The incidence of Alkaptonuria: A study in chemical individuality," *Lancet,* 2: 1616–1620.

Glass, Bentley, Milton S. Sacks, Elsa F. Jahn, and Charles Hess, 1952, "Genetic drift in a religious isolate: An analysis of the causes of variation in blood group and other gene frequencies in a small population," *The American Naturalist,* 86: 145–159.

Goldstein, M. S., 1943, *Demographic and bodily changes in descendants of Mexican immigrants.* Austin, Texas: University of Texas, Institute of Latin American Studies.

Graydon, J. J., N. M. Semple, R. T. Simmons, and S. Franken, 1958, "Blood groups in Pygmies of the Wissellakes in Netherlands New Guinea," *American Journal of Physical Anthropology,* new series, 16: 149–171.

Gregg, Alan, 1955, "A medical aspect of the population problem," *Science,* 121: 681–682.

Hardin, Garrett, 1959, *Nature and man's fate.* New York: Holt, Rinehart and Winston.

Hooton, Earnest Albert, 1930, *Indians of Pecos Pueblo,* New Haven: Yale University Press.

———, 1946, *Up from the ape,* rev. ed. New York: Macmillan.

Hopkins, David M., 1959, "Cenozoic history of the Bering land bridge," *Science,* 129: 1519–1528.

Horowitz, N. H., 1945, "On the evolution of biochemical syntheses," *Proceedings of the National Academy of Sciences,* 31: 153–157.

Howell, F. Clark, 1955, "The age of the australopithecines of Southern Africa," *American Journal of Physical Anthropology,* new series, 13: 635–662.

———, 1959, "The Villafranchian and human origins," *Science* 130: 831–844.

Howells, William W., 1944, *Mankind so far.* New York: Doubleday, p. 44.

Hulse, Frederick S., 1955, "Technological advance and major racial stocks," *Human Biology,* 27: 184–192.

———, 1957, "Some factors influencing the relative proportions of human racial stocks," *Cold Spring Harbor Symposium on Quantitative Biology,* 22: 33–45.

Hunt, Edward E., Jr., 1959, "Anthropometry, genetics and racial history," *American Anthropologist,* 61: 64–87.

Hürzeler, Johannes, 1958, "Oreopithecus bambolii Gervais, a preliminary report," *Verh. Naturf. Ges. Basel,* 69: 1–48.

Huxley, Julian, 1943, *Evolution, the modern synthesis.* New York: Harper & Brothers.

Huxley, Thomas H., 1863, *Evidence as to man's place in nature.* New York.

Ito, Paul K., 1942, "Comparative biometrical study of physique of Japanese women born and reared under different environments," *Human Biology,* 14: 279–351.

Keith, Sir Arthur, 1925, *The antiquity of man.* London.

Klineberg, Otto, 1935, *Race differences.* New York: Harper & Brothers.

Kroeber, A. L., 1948, *Anthropology,* new ed., revised. New York: Harcourt, Brace and Company.

LaBarre, Weston, 1954, *The human animal.* Chicago: University of Chicago Press.

LaFarge, Oliver, 1960, "The enduring Indian," *Scientific American,* 202: 37–45.

Landsteiner, Karl, 1945, *The specificity of serological reactions.* Cambridge, Mass.: Harvard University Press.

———, and P. Levene, 1927, "A New agglutinable factor differentiating individual human bloods," *Proceedings of the Society of Experimental Biology,* New York, 24: 600–602.

———, and A. S. Wiener, 1940, "An agglutinable factor in human blood recognized by immune sera for rhesus blood," *Proceedings of the Society of Experimental Biology,* New York, 43: 223.

Lasker, G. W., 1946, "Migration and physical differentiation," *American Journal of Physical Anthropology,* new series, 4: 273–300.

———, 1952, "Environmental growth factors and selective migration," *Human Biology,* 24: 262–289.

———, 1954A, "Human evolution in contemporary communities," *Southwestern Journal of Anthropology,* 10: 353–365.

———, 1954B, "The question of physical selection of Mexican migrants to the U. S. A.," *Human Biology,* 26: 52–58.

Laughlin, William S., 1960, "Aspects of current physical anthropology: method and theory," *Southwestern Journal of Anthropology*, 16: 75–92.

Layrisse, Miguel, 1958, "Anthropological considerations of the Diego (Di^a) antigen," *American Journal of Physical Anthropology*, new series, 16: 173–195.

Leakey, L. S. B., 1959, "The newly discovered skull from Olduvai: first photographs of the complete skull," *Illustrated London News*, 235: 288–289.

Levene, Philip, 1958, "The influence of the ABO system on Rh hemolitic disease," *Human Biology*, 30: 14–28.

————, and R. E. Stetson, 1939, "An unusual case of intragroup agglutination," *Journal of the American Medical Association*, 113: 126–127.

Linnaeus, Carolus, 1758, *Systema Naturae per Regna tria naturae secundum classes, ordines, genera, species cum characteribus, differentiis, synonymis, locis,* editio decima, reformata. Stockholm: Laurentii Salvii.

McBurney, C. B. M., J. C. Trevor, and L. H. Wells, 1953, "The Haua Fteah fossil jaw," *Journal of the Royal Anthropological Institute of Great Britain and Ireland*, 83: 71–85.

McCown, T. D., and A. Keith, 1939, *The stone age of Mount Carmel,* Volume II. *The fossil human remains from the Levalloiso-Mousterian.* Oxford: Clarendon Press.

Markowitz, Stephen D., 1955, "Retardation in growth of children in Europe and Asia during World War II," *Human Biology*, 27: 258–273.

Marston, A. T., 1937, "The Swanscombe skull," *Journal of the Royal Anthropological Institute*, 67: 339–406.

Mednick, Lois W., and S. L. Washburn, 1956, "The role of the sutures in the growth of the braincase of the infant pig," *American Journal of Physical Anthropology*, new series, 14: 175–191.

Monge, Carlos, 1953, "Biological basis of human behavior," *Anthropology today: an encyclopedic inventory,* pp. 127–144, A. L. Kroeber, ed. Chicago: University of Chicago Press.

Montagu, M. F. Ashley, 1951, *Introduction to physical anthropology,* rev. ed. Springfield, Ill.: C. C. Thomas.

Morant, G. M., 1930–1931, "Studies of Palaeolithic man." Part IV, "A biometric study of the upper Palaeolithic skulls of Europe and of their relationships to earlier and later types," *Annals of Eugenics,* 4: 109–214.

Motulsky, Arno G., 1960, "Metabolic polymorphisms and the role of infectious diseases in human evolution," *Human Biology*, 32: 28–62.

Mourant, A. E., 1954, *The distribution of the human blood groups.* Oxford: Blackwell Scientific Publications.

Neel, James V., 1957, "Human hemoglobin types, their epidemiologic significance," *New England Journal of Medicine*, 256: 161–171.

Newman, H. H., F. M. Freeman, and K. J. Holzinger, 1937, *Twins: A study of heredity and environment.* Chicago: University of Chicago Press.

Nissen, H. W., 1931, "A field study of the chimpanzee, observations of chimpanzee behavior and environment in Western French Guinea," *Comparative Psychology Monographs*, Vol. 8, No. 1, serial no. 36. Baltimore: The Johns Hopkins University Press.

Oakley, Kenneth P., "The fluorine dating method," *Yearbook of Physical Anthropology—1949*, pp. 44–52.

Pearson, Karl, 1896, "Mathematical contributions to the theory of evolution. III. Regression, heredity and panmixia," *Philosophical Transactions of the Royal Society of London*, series A, 187: 253–318. Reprinted in *Karl Pearson's Early Statistical Papers*, Cambridge University Press, pp. 113–178 (1948).

Pei, Wen-chung, 1957, "Découverte en Chine d'une mandibule de singe géant," *l'Anthropologie*, 61: 77–83. See also Hillaby, John, 1957, "The Kwangsi jaw," *American Journal of Physical Anthropology*, new series, 15: 281–285.

Race, R. R., and Ruth Sanger, 1954, *Blood groups in man,* 2d ed. Springfield, Ill.: C. C. Thomas.

Retzius, Anders Adolf, 1860, "De Brachycephaliska och Dolichocephaliska Folkslagens Geografiska Utbredning Forklaring til attoljande Karta," *K. Vet. Akad. Fork.*, No. 2, not seen, pp. 99–101.

Reynolds, Earle L., 1951, "The distribution of subcutaneous fat in childhood and adolescence," *Monographs of the Society for Research in Child Development, Inc.,* Vol. 15, No. 2, serial no. 50.

Robinson, J. T., 1954, "The genera and species of the Australopithecinae," *American Journal of Physical Anthropology*, new series, 12: 181–200.

Sanghvi, L. D., and V. R. Khanolkar, 1949, "Data relating to seven genetical characters in six endogamous groups in Bombay," *Annals of Eugenics,* 15: 52–64.

Sax, Karl, 1956, "The population explosion," *Foreign Policy Association Headline Series,* No. 120, p. 12.

Scammon, Richard E., 1927, "The first seriatim study of human growth," *American Journal of Physical Anthropology*, 10: 329–336.

Schultz, Adolph H., 1937, "Proportions, variability and asymmetries of the long bones of the limbs and the clavicles in man and apes," *Human Biology,* 9: 281–328.

Shapiro, H. L., 1931, "The Chinese population in Hawaii: Preliminary paper prepared for the Fourth General Session of the Institute of Pacific Relations." New York: American Council, Institute of Pacific Relations, pp. 3–29.

———, 1939, *Migration and environment.* New York: Oxford University Press.

———, 1952, "Revised version of UNESCO statement on race," *American Journal of Physical Anthropology,* new series, 10: 363–368.

Simmons, R. T., and J. J. Graydon, 1957, "A blood group genetical survey in Eastern and Central Polynesians," *American Journal of Physical Anthropology,* new series, 15: 357–366.

Simons, Elwyn L., 1959, "An anthropoid frontal bone from the Fayum Oligocene of Egypt: the oldest skull fragment of a higher primate," *American Museum Novitates,* number 1976, 1–16.

Simpson, G. G., 1945, "The principles of classification and a classification of mammals," *Bulletin of the American Museum of Natural History,* New York, No. 85.

Spuhler, J. N., 1959, "Somatic paths to culture," *Human Biology,* 31: 1–13.

Straus, William L. Jr., 1949, "The riddle of man's ancestry," *The Quarterly Review of Biology,* 24: 200–223. Reprinted in *Yearbook of Physical Anthropology—1949, pp.* 134–157.

———, 1957, *"Oreopithecus bambolii," Science,* 126: 345–346.

———, and A. J. E. Cave, 1957, "Pathology and posture of Neanderthal man," *Quarterly Review of Biology,* 32: 348–363.

Thieme, Frederick P., 1952, "The population as a unit of study," *American Anthropologist,* 54: 504–509.

Urey, H. C., 1952, *The planets.* New Haven: Yale University Press.

Vallois, H. V., 1949, "The Fontéchevade fossil men," *American Journal of Physical Anthropology,* new series, 7: 339–362.

———, 1956, "The pre-mousterian human mandible from Montmaurin," *American Journal of Physical Anthropology,* new series, 14: 319–323.

Walcher, G., 1905, "Ueber die Entstehung von Brachy- und Dolichocephalie durch willkurliche Beeinflusseng des Kindlichen Schadels, *Zentralblat fur Gynakologie,* 29: 193–196.

Washburn, S. L., 1951, "The new physical anthropology," *Transactions of the New York Academy of Sciences,* series II, 13: 298–304. Reprinted in *Yearbook of Physical Anthropology—1951,* 7: 124–130.

————, 1959, "Speculation on the interrelations of the history of tools and biological evolution," *Human Biology,* 31: 21–31.

Watson, J. D., and F. H. C. Crick, 1953. "The structure of D. N. A.," *Cold Spring Harbor Symposia on Quantitative Biology,* 18: 123–131.

Weidenreich, Franz, 1927, "Der Schadel von Weimar-Ehringsdorf," *Verhandl. der Gesellschaft fur Phys. Anthrop.* Bd. 2, 34–41, Stuttgart.

————, 1936, "The mandibles of *Sinanthropus pekinensis:* a comparative study," *Palaeontologia Sinica,* series D, 7: 1–162.

————, 1937, "The dentition of *Sinanthropus pekinensis:* a comparative odontography of the hominids," 2 vol., *Palaeontologia Sinica,* new series D, No. 1, whole series No. 101.

————, 1941, "The extremity bones of *Sinanthropus pekinensis,*" *Palaeontologia Sinica,* new series D, No. 5, whole series No. 115: 1–150.

————, 1943, "The skull of *Sinanthropus pekinensis:* a comparative study on a primitive hominid skull, *Palaeontologia Sinica,* new series D, No. 10, whole series No. 127: 1–484.

————, 1939, "On the earliest representatives of modern mankind recovered on the soil of East Asia," *Peking Natural History Bulletin,* 13: 161–174.

————, and G. H. R. von Koenigswald, 1951, "Morphology of Solo man," *Anthropological Papers of the American Museum of Natural History,* 43: 205–290.

Wendorf, F. A. D. Krieger, and C. C. Albritton, 1955, *The Midland discovery.* Austin, Texas: University of Texas Press.

White, Leslie A., 1959, summary review in Spuhler, J. N., ed. *The evolution of man's capacity for culture.* Detroit, Mich.: Wayne State University Press, pp. 74–79.

White, Robert M., 1952, "Some applications of physical anthropology," *Journal of the Washington Academy of Sciences,* 42: 65–71.

Woo, Ju-kang, 1956, "Human fossils found in China and their significance in human evolution," *Scientia Sinica,* 5: 389–397.

————, and Tze-kuei Chao, 1959, "New discovery of *Sinanthropus* mandible from Choukoutien," *Vertebrata Palasiatica,* 3: 169–172.

————, and Ru-ca Peng, 1959, "Fossil human skull of early paleoanthropic stage found at Mapa, Shaoquan, Kwantung Province," *Vertebrata Palasiatica,* 3: 176–182.

Wright, Sewall, 1932, "The roles of mutation, inbreeding, crossbreeding and selection in evolution," *Proceedings of the Sixth International Congress of Genetics,* 1: 356–366.

————, 1938, "Size of population and breeding structure in relation to evolution," *Science,* 87: 430–431.

Zapfe, Helmuth, 1958, "The skeleton of *Pliopithecus* (Epipliopithecus) *vindobonensis* Zapfe and Hürzeler," *American Journal of Physical Anthropology,* new series, 16: 441–455.

Zeuner, Frederick E., 1958, *Dating the past,* 4th ed., London: Methuen and Company.

Zuckerman, Solly, 1932, *The social life of monkeys and apes.* London: Kegan Paul.

————, 1933, *Functional affinities of man, monkeys and apes.* New York: Harcourt, Brace and Company.

Index

Index

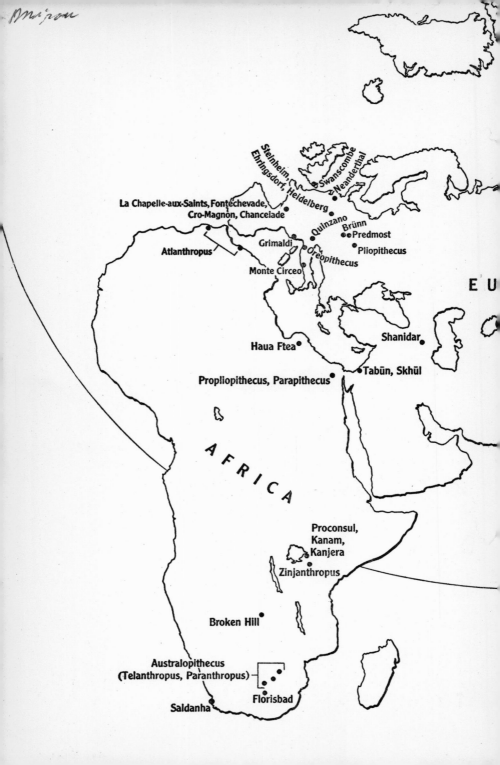